Diagnosis Corruption

Fraud in Latin America's Public Hospitals

Rafael Di Tella and
William D. Savedoff

Editors

Inter-American Development Bank
Washington, D.C.
2001

Latin American Research Network
Inter-American Development Bank

The Inter-American Development Bank created the Latin American Research Network in 1991 in order to strengthen policy formulation and contribute to the development policy agenda in Latin America.

Through a competitive bidding process, the network provides grant funding to leading Latin American research centers to conduct studies on economic and social issues selected by the Bank in consultation with the region's development community.

Most of the studies are comparative, which allows the Bank to build its knowledge base and draw on lessons from experiences in macoreconomic and financial policy, modernization of the State, regulation, poverty and income distribution, social services, and employment.

Individual country studies are available as working papers and are also available in PDF format on the Internet at http://www.iadb.org/oce/RED_working_papers.cfm

© 2001   Inter-American Development Bank
          1300 New York Avenue, N.W.
          Washington, D.C. 20577

Cover images: © 2001 PhotoDisc, Inc

To order this book, contact:
IDB Bookstore
Tel: 1-877-PUBS IDB/(202) 623-1753   Fax: (202) 623-1709
E-mail: idb-books@iadb.org   www.iadb.org/pub

The opinions and points of view expressed in this publication are the authors' and do not necessarily reflect those of the Inter-American Development Bank.

Cataloging-in-Publication data provided by the
Inter-American Development Bank
Felipe Herrera Library

Diagnosis corruption : fraud in Latin America's public hospitals / Raphael Di Tella and William D. Savedoff, editors.
      "Latin American Research Network"—Verso t.p.
      ISBN: 1931003114
      Includes bibliographical references.
1. Public hospitals—Latin America. 2. Health facilities—Latin America—Corrupt practices. 3. Health care reform—Latin America. I. Di Tella, Raphael. II. Savedoff, William D. III. Inter-American Development Bank. Latin American Research Network.
362.11 D534 – dc21   LCCN: 01-097059

CONTENTS

ACKNOWLEDGMENTS

This book would never have been written without the initial interest and enthusiasm of James Spinner and Ricardo Hausmann, who charged us with developing a new way of studying corruption. Rosina de Souza was an essential member of the project, sharing responsibility for coordinating the research and informing our work with her legal expertise and extensive knowledge of issues related to corruption. Along the way, the overall research project benefited from the comments and suggestions of many colleagues, including Antonio Ugalde, Gerard La Forgia, and the many participants who offered feedback and encouragement in various seminars in Washington and Mexico. Special mention should be made of contributions by Jaime Chang, Gabriel Ortiz de Zevallos, and Maria Antonia Remenyi to the chapter on Peru; Damián Staffa, Diego Rabasa, and Fernanda Martijena on Argentina; Angel Ayalón on Venezuela; and Taty Apraez, Mario García, Lorena Hernández and Alvaro Muriel on Colombia. Maria Angelica Albino provided an important boost to the book by synthesizing many of the results from the case studies; and Martha Chavez assisted in making revisions in the texts. Norelis Betancourt, Raquel Gomez, Rita Funaro, Ron Weber, John Dunn Smith, and Yoli Prado need to be recognized as the dream team that kept the administrative and publication nightmares out of our dreams.

Due to the nature of the research, it is not possible to openly acknowledge all of the public officials who opened their books and offices to us. However, we can express thanks to the Health Secretariat of the City of Buenos Aires and, in particular, Amanda Rubilar, Sub-Secretary of Strategic Management, as well as Beatriz Londoño, former Secretary of Health in Bogota, for providing access to records and hospitals under their supervision. We would also like to thank the many other government and hospital officials, and respondents, without whom this book would not only be impossible, but worthless. They are the ones taking risks every day to combat the corrupt activities identified and discussed here. We dedicate this book to them and hope it may contribute in some small way to making their lives easier, and to supporting their efforts.

PREFACE

Latin Americans have complained about government corruption for decades, but only recently has it become a serious issue among national governments and the subject of international summits. Corruption is increasingly seen as a critical obstacle to social development, to the creation of well-functioning democratic institutions, and to economic progress. Yet our understanding of what encourages or discourages people from betraying the public trust is still very limited. Empirical studies of corruption began in earnest only in the last decade. These studies have looked at general measures of corruption in a country, or examined specific government functions like taxation, customs administration, or licensing.

This Latin American Research Network study advances beyond previous efforts in several important ways. First, it looks at corruption in a public institution of great social significance — public hospitals. Secondly, it generates a new class of measures for corruption, using information on prices paid for hospital supplies and comparing them across similar facilities to detect overpayments. Finally, it sheds light on the kinds of policies that may be most successful at reducing corruption, namely increased transparency, monitoring, and effective application of penalties. Because these recommendations come out of a particular context, their policy implications are more precise and practical than those from more-aggregated studies.

The demands for strengthening democracy and for making government services work for the people are more powerful today than ever before. By supporting these demands with research, debate, and greater transparency, it may be possible to turn the tide against corruption in our region.

Guillermo Calvo
Chief Economist
Inter-American Development Bank

CHAPTER 1

Shining Light in Dark Corners

Rafael Di Tella and William D. Savedoff

This chapter explores the problems of measuring, analyzing, and combating corruption, highlighting problems encountered in Latin America's public hospitals. It reviews progress in the study of corruption, including recent advances in measuring the incidence and effect of these illicit activities. Using seven case studies of abuses identified in hospitals, it argues that objective data on corruption can be collected, analyzed, and used to study different forms of corruption. The chapter also discusses how such data can aid in designing anticorruption programs. It then summarizes findings about the character and quantity of abuses found in Latin America's public hospitals, which siphon off government resources and compromise the health system's ability to provide needed care. Finally, it identifies features in the structure of incentives, accountability, and transparency that can be used to reduce the scope and costs of corruption in these important public institutions.

Introduction

Corruption. The word was virtually unprintable in official publications of Latin America until the end of the 1990s, when fighting corruption became a public battlecry. The most visible sign of this change came in 1996, when members of the Organization of American States signed the Inter-American Convention Against Corruption. Presidents as different as Vicente Fox of Mexico and Hugo Chávez of Venezuela have made the fight against corruption a core of their political programs. Multilateral organizations such as the International Monetary Fund, the World Bank, and the Inter-American Development Bank have begun to publicly discuss corruption as an impediment to development, and even begun to finance operations to reduce corruption in tax administration, customs agencies, and the judiciary.[1] Whatever caused the political winds to shift on this issue, it has clearly provided an opportunity for improving the rule of law, the effectiveness of public administration, and the transparency of public debate.

But capitalizing on this opportunity requires practical actions, which must be informed if they are to succeed. How much corruption is there? What are the worst abuses? How should priorities be set for corrective action? What are the sources of corruption and how can they be stemmed? Answering these questions requires not only information but also analysis. Fortunately, the increased attention on corruption in recent years has spurred data collection that shines new light on behaviors that, by their very nature, seek to remain hidden.

Empirical studies of corruption have generally focused on areas involving government permits, licenses, or taxes. The government's coercive power to police imports and exports, regulate zoning, or raise general revenues is contrasted with the private gain officials can obtain through delaying and changing decisions in return for bribes or kickbacks. One area not much discussed in the literature on corruption, particularly in Latin America, is health care. Health expenditures represent more than 7 percent of Latin America's GDP, with about 3.5 percent of GDP spent by the public sector alone. More than two-thirds of the public expenditures go to build, maintain, and operate public hospitals and provide related services, creating wide latitude for potential corruption.

Using studies of public-sector hospitals, this book addresses several issues. First, it demonstrates that objective data on corruption can be collected, analyzed, and used to stem corruption. Second, it measures and characterizes the abuse found in Latin America's public hospitals that drains government resources and compromises the health system's ability to serve the people. Finally, it identifies what features in the structure of incentives, accountability, and transparency can be used to reduce the scope and costs of this corruption.

---

[1] Recent examples are several technical assistance operations of the Inter-American Development Bank that were approved in 1998 and 1999. These include "Strengthening of Supreme Audit Institutions in Auditing Fraud and Corruption," "Incorporation of Information Technology in Public Procurement," and "Latin American Development and Transparency" aimed at enhancing transparency in public accounts for five countries.

It is important to emphasize that this is only a first step in analyzing a very complex and hidden phenomenon. Common practices of petty bribery or theft are often easier (and less dangerous) to identify than specific cases of large-scale graft. One must also distinguish patterns of individual acts from orchestrated activities that can truly be called organized crime. Because the case studies in this book were designed to focus on fraud and misuse of funds *within* hospitals, they exclude much of the corruption related to the ministries and institutes that build, maintain, and operate hospitals — a topic that remains for future research. Indeed, the measurements of corruption in these studies must be interpreted in light of their specificity, and we must exercise great caution in deciding whether or not these measures can serve as proxies for other kinds of illegal activity in the hospital or health sector.

Conjectures in Search of Evidence

Corruption is a major social problem. Economists and other social scientists have long recognized this and, at least since Myrdal (1968), have written extensively on the topic. Yet for decades understanding the causes and consequences of corruption advanced very slowly. Whenever a theory was presented to explain one aspect of the problem, a contradictory theory seemed to follow immediately in its wake.

A good example of this pendulum in theory formation can be seen in efforts to articulate how corruption affects development. Even as researchers were beginning to fit pieces of the puzzle together to explain how corruption impedes development and reduces the rate of economic growth, a number of alternative theories appeared that maintained corruption was actually good for development. Some argued, for example, that corruption was a way to introduce bonus payments into the bureaucracy, making government more efficient by providing incentives to perform. The notion that corruption was a way around red tape was often summarized with the dictum: "There are very few things worse for a country than having a corrupt, obtrusive bureaucracy, and one of them is having an honest, obtrusive bureaucracy."

The underlying problem with these debates was the lack of means for resolving them. The study of corruption did not meet all of the standard criteria developed by scholars to qualify it as a "science" (Blaug, 1980). It was not so much that these efforts failed to pass Popper's "demarcation criterion" between science and nonscience. The theories, after all, produced statements that could, at least in principle, be falsified empirically. The fundamental problem was the absence of data to guide scientific inquiry. The unavailability of corruption data meant that rhetorical arguments took the place of hypothesis testing.

This unsatisfactory state of affairs continued until Mauro (1995) started a small revolution by publishing the first empirical paper on corruption. His contribution was to introduce into economics a cross-country corruption data set that was developed by Business International (BI), a firm that later became a subsidiary of The Economist Intelligence Unit. This data set was part of the information gathering that BI used to construct country risk indices. The "political situation" was one index of risk that BI had begun using around 1980, and "corruption" was one of its aspects. The measurements used were subjective in nature. Correspondents based in each country were asked to describe local conditions, assigning a number from 1 to 10 to describe "the degree to which business transactions involve corrupt payments." All informants were instructed to use a similar methodology, and their reports were further checked for comparability at the regional level and at BI's headquarters. Since this information was sold to institutional investors for substantial sums, there was some reason to believe that it had value. Put another way, an argument of revealed preference could be made in defense of the use of subjective data: The market was using it. These data are shown in Table 1.1.

Mauro (1995) used this data to address the controversy about the effect of corruption on growth. He showed that the association was negative. Furthermore he divided the sample into countries with lots of red tape and countries with few bureaucratic impediments. He then demonstrated that the estimated negative effect of corruption on growth and investment did not vary across the two subsamples, negating arguments that bribes had a beneficial role, that they were "grease in the wheels of commerce" as business pundits often claimed.

Other studies soon followed. For example, Hines (1995) used the same BI data to study the effect of the Foreign Corrupt Practices Act (FCPA) on U.S. business abroad. He was able to show that the FCPA was detrimental to American commercial interests.

Another study, by Ades and Di Tella (1999), turned to the causes of corruption. That study focused on one of the first questions asked by econo-

Table 1.1 The International Business Corruption Index (1980–83)

BI = 0	0 < BI < 1	1 < BI < 2	2 < BI < 4	4 < BI < 6	6 < BI < 9
Australia	Belgium	Angola	Argentina	Algeria	Egypt
Canada	Chile	Austria	Cameroon	Bangladesh	Ghana
France	Denmark	Hong Kong	Dominican Republic	Brazil	Haiti
Iraq	Finland	Japan	Greece	Colombia	Indonesia
Netherlands	Germany	Jordan	Italy	Ecuador	Iran
New Zealand	Ireland	Nicaragua	Ivory Coast	India	Liberia
Norway	Israel	South Africa	Kuwait	Jamaica	Mexico
Singapore	U.K.	Uruguay	Malaysia	Kenya	Nigeria
Switzerland	Sweden	Zimbabwe	Peru	Korea	Thailand
United States			Portugal	Morocco	Zaire
			Spain	Pakistan	
			Sri Lanka	Panama	
			Taiwan	Philippines	
			Trinidad/Tobago	Saudi Arabia	
			Turkey	Venezuela	

Source: Reproduced in Ades and Di Tella (1997).

Note: The BI corruption index covers 68 countries and rates them from 0 to 10, with 10 being the most corrupt.

mists who studied corruption, the role of competition as a limiting factor (Rose-Ackerman, 1978). That is, corruption should not be present in a perfectly competitive environment since there are no excess profits from which to pay bribes.[2] The paper by Ades and Di Tella used subjective indices to show that there was evidence to support the hypothesis that competition reduces the opportunities for corruption.

In addition to the BI data, Ades and Di Tella used a second data set, from the *World Competitiveness Report* (*WCR*), which is a business publication of the World Economic Forum in Switzerland. The *WCR* data set on

---

[2] Bliss and Di Tella (1997) show that one cannot use the number of competitors as an indicator of competition since that is in itself endogenous. They also derive conditions under which competition will "kill" corruption.

corruption comes from an annual survey of top and mid-level managers in the leading firms in each of the countries covered. Since 1989 (with results first published in 1990) the surveys have included a question on corruption, asking well over a thousand executives in at least 32 countries to rate "the degree to which improper practices (like corruption) prevail in the public sphere." An advantage of the *WCR* over the BI data is that it surveys people with an intimate knowledge of business practices in each of the countries covered. However, the apparent lack of a centralized office to consolidate the answers of *WCR* respondents could be a drawback in a cross-section study, raising a question about the comparability of results between countries. The fact that survey participants represent companies that are successful and internationally oriented only partially allays this concern.

Since the first studies opened the gate, the field has been flooded with dozens of papers using these and other indices.[3] All the indices, however, share one feature: subjectivity. At the end of the day, these data on corruption in different countries come from a subjective assessment by an individual or a group of individuals.

At the same time that researchers have been developing a proliferation of indices, movement has also been taking place among international organizations, particularly since the Asian crisis. The International Monetary Fund, for example, now routinely incorporates, in the letters of intent it signs with member countries, targets for reducing corruption. These are based on the countries taking actions to reduce corruption. Some have argued, however, that the terms are too vague, leaving considerable room for corrupt practices to continue. Critics therefore have pushed for the use of indicators of progress, something like the indices being used in the corruption literature.

The movement from literature to practice, however, confronts a major potential stumbling block — the countries in question must agree to participate. That is, they have to be willing to let their resources and their access to IMF credit be affected by subjective indices. This is unlikely. Recent experience with the aggregate corruption index produced and publicized by Trans-

---

[3] See also Wei (1997). Other papers that use subjective data on corruption include Mauro (1998), Tanzi and Davoodi (1997), Treisman (1998), Kaufmann and Wei (1999), Svensson (1999), La Porta et al. (1999), Alesina and Weder (1999), Gatti (1999), and Fisman and Gatti (2000).

parency International (TI) is telling. TI's index combines the average of a number of subjective indices coming from so-called "polls of experts" and other survey measures. As the index has grown in influence, governments of countries with bad rankings have vociferously complained about the methods of compilation. Having scrutinized the index, some countries — Bolivia and Argentina, among them — have accused TI of tampering with the information and have threatened to take legal action.

One alternative is to rely on only the more precise indices. Intuitively some seem considerably more reliable than others. This is the case, for example, with the data set gathered by Peter Neuman and his collaborators at *Impulse*, a German business publication. Survey respondents are German business people (typically exporters) who regularly deal with countries being covered. On average, 10 persons were interviewed for each country, with a minimum standard of three respondents per country. Perhaps the biggest advantage of this data set is its effort to rein in subjectivity by asking survey participants to estimate the kickback per deal (as a percentage of the deal's value) that would have to be paid in order to conduct business in each country. In addition to shifting from a normative to a more quantitative evaluation, the survey group's homogeneity (German exporters with practical business experience in each country) further reduces the likelihood of extraneous noise contaminating the results. The data was published in 1994 and covers 103 countries.[4]

Another alternative is to try to improve the methods used in aggregating multiple indices. Since the data come from many different sources, which do not always agree with each other, it is important to have a measure of how precise the data for a country is. The traditional approach reports the average for each country plus a measure of the deviation from the mean. Kaufmann et al. (1999) have recently proposed a novel approach, based on principal components, as a simple way of aggregating multiple corruption indicators. Their method relies on weighting the different polls. Take, for example, countries A, B, and C, which are evaluated in polls x, y, and z. Imagine that country A is ranked with the same corruption number in x and y but receives a different corruption number from polling company z. This is repeated for country B, which is ranked the same by x and y, but not by z. In

---

[4] Ades and Di Tella (1997) use the data to study optimal intervention to correct market failures (related to industrial policy) when bureaucratic corruption is a source of concern.

trying to then measure the corruption level of country C, one would tend to discount the verdict of z. That is, in some sense, one would like to reward consensus.

Figure 1.1, drawn from Kaufmann et al. (1999) shows the data. The horizontal axis lists the countries by their estimated levels of corruption. The vertical bars around the country's estimate are the 90 percent confidence interval. The authors observe that, in general, these intervals are large. There are two reasons. First, some countries appear in a small number of polls, and estimates based on few sources are relatively noisy. Second, some sources of corruption data are "better" in the sense of having a higher signal-to-noise ratio (i.e., they are more informative than other sources).

For large groups of countries the confidence intervals overlap, which means that there is no statistically significant difference among their corruption scores. In other words, it is misleading to focus on very precise

Figure 1.1 Composite Index of Corruption

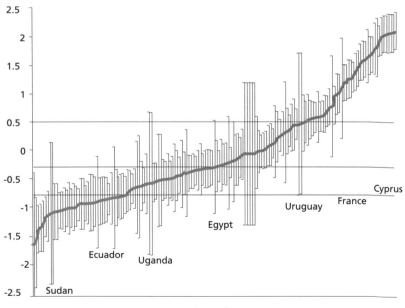

Countries

Source: Kaufmann et al. (1999).

rankings of countries. The authors suggest it might be more useful to rank countries by clustering them into a small number of groups (maybe three).

Searching for Harder Data

In light of the difficulties with governance indicators, an alternative approach is to abandon subjective indices and to try to develop more precise measures of corruption, based on hard data. A paper by Goel and Rich (1989) used the number of convictions on bribery charges against public servants at the state level in the U.S. Since such an indicator mixes the amount of corruption with the degree of enforcement of anticorruption laws, this data is unlikely to have the precision required. Put simply, states with ineffective institutions for detecting, apprehending, and convicting dishonest public officials may appear cleaner than those with effective institutions, even if the former have more corruption. Objections to this indicator are not limited to the question of fixed effects. Some of the dimensions are time varying, perhaps the most important being anticorruption initiatives. Such audit-related actions are often politically driven and will likely change over time. Furthermore, reliance on this indicator for identifying the depth of the problem or pegging performance to policy solutions can easily be defeated. Countries that want to appear cleaner only need to stop prosecuting offenders.

Another approach infers the amount of corruption by calculating "residuals," or the remainder left after accounting for legal or proper activities. For example, in a classic article Cagan (1958) estimated the size of the informal economy in the U.S. by using survey information about cash-holdings, statistics of total cash supplied by the Federal Reserve Bank, and estimates of the ratio of legitimate economic activity to legitimate cash-holdings. By assuming that the rate of transactions (the "velocity of money") in the informal economy keeps some relationship with that in the formal economy, the magnitude of unreported transactions can be deduced.

In their paper, Lewis et al. (1996) demonstrate how such a method could be applied to hospitals. After doing a careful analysis of the unit costs of services in a particular hospital, they were able to estimate what total spending *ought* to be by multiplying these unit prices by the quantity of services provided. This estimated cost of services was 68 percent lower than actual spending, indicating that almost one-third of total expenditures were unaccounted. This excess represented some combination of gross misman-agement, diversion of funds, and theft of materials and supplies.

In a similarly detailed study (La Forgia, 1990), researchers counted high-value medications in the hospital's stores at the beginning of each day to establish a baseline. The difference with the next day's inventory was then compared with the amount of medications that should have been used, based on written prescriptions. The difference represented an estimate of the magnitude of theft — and it was large.

Within this broad category of methods that infer the extent of corruption from objective data are those that look specifically at *procurement prices* relative to the "actual" or "legitimate" price. Even with this kind of objective price data, however, it is inherently difficult to measure corruption. When kickbacks and graft occur in buying large, infrequently purchased items, there is little evidence to show whether the price was excessive. For example, when the procurement officer in the ministry of defense buys a submarine for millions of dollars, one has no clue if this is outrageous or if the officer got a bargain. To determine guilt often requires lengthy and costly procedures. And even after such processes, the picture often remains murky when equipment has been custom built or other considerations are factored in. But while this is true with large and infrequent purchases, such as the submarine, which are bought and sold in "thin markets," one might think it would be easy to measure corruption in the case of regular purchases of relatively small and homogeneous products, like syringes. In such a case, indeed, the observability of a market price and consequently greater ease in detecting corruption should make abuses in these purchases uncommon.

Despite this expectation, the case studies presented in the following chapters demonstrate that, in fact, the prices paid by different hospitals for basic, homogeneous inputs vary enormously. These variations cannot be explained by differences in the quality or brands of the products purchased. Nor can they be explained by transportation costs from the hospitals to the supplier since the hospitals are often located in the same geographical areas. These price differences persist after one controls for the size of the purchase, the method of payment, the credit terms, or the time of purchase. One explanation for the differences might be awareness by purchasing agents that such transactions are not systematically reviewed. In fact, previous work on input procurement in public hospitals in Argentina showed that input prices dropped sharply when the public health sector authorities began to monitor the purchasing process (Di Tella, 1997).

Yet there are also more benign possibilities. Prices are subject to many different influences, and the process of price formation is still poorly understood. That is, prices are "noisy" indicators, and the information about corruption they may contain can be obscured by the effects of other factors. For example, chapter 4 demonstrates that in Buenos Aires there was almost as much variation in prices across time in any particular hospital as there was across hospitals at any particular time. This kind of "equilibrium price dispersion" on the buyer's side is surprising. It suggests that using input prices as a measure of corruption must take into account the presence of considerable noise levels.[5] This is not particularly problematic if the data are used as a dependent variable, but suggests caution otherwise. We are not aware of any previous documentation of this theoretic type of price dispersion in purchases, and it certainly suggests that to better understand input prices paid by the public sector it is important to know the behavior of input prices paid by large *private* organizations.

Like the other approaches in this section that rely on observable or public information to infer the magnitude of illegal activity, what seems very attractive initially becomes less so on closer examination. These indices tend to be useful only in particular contexts (e.g., the case of U.S. money supply in an economy for which unreported transactions are, by and large, illegal ones), costly to obtain (e.g., the case of detailed estimates of costs or theft), or subject to conflicting interpretations (e.g., procurement prices).

This suggests that the distinction between "hard" and "soft" data in measuring corruption is somewhat artificial. In fact one should not presume that an index based on perceptions that come from a survey is automatically dubious. Much of the data that is widely used in economics comes from surveys — including unemployment figures, household income and expenditures, and demand elasticities. Objections are raised, however, that survey data on corruption is usually subjective in the sense that it only registers opinions. Furthermore the answers are frequently in the form of rankings, which creates problems associated with "cardinality" (does the difference between a "2" and a "3" on the scale mean the same as a difference

---

[5] Equilibrium price dispersion is analyzed in Reinganum (1979), Salop and Stiglitz (1977), *inter alia*.

between "5" and "6"? does a ranking of "4" mean the same thing to different people?). Some surveys address this problem by using more-sophisticated questions. For example the German exporters index, cited in the previous section, uses a quantitative question ("In a deal with country x, what is the percentage of the total price that must be paid in bribes?"). It is also true that different indices may correlate well with one another, suggesting some shared common structure, and this lends them credibility despite the relative "subjectivity" or "softness" of the indicators.

Ultimately the choice of index depends on its intended uses, which will determine the relative importance assigned to its reliability, precision, and cost. Corruption indices derived from surveys of expert opinions, for instance, may be cheaper and more readily available from existing sources, but also less precise. They also may be more useful for cross-country comparisons by imposing some degree of homogeneity for criteria and among the observers. In contrast, indices based on collecting registered information or on sophisticated questionnaires designed to elicit information of the respondent's collaboration in illicit acts are sometimes, but not always, costly. Although certainly less commonly available, they promise greater precision for guiding specific policies in a particular sector or country. Essentially, the best choice is to obtain the data most relevant to the problem. The case studies in this volume make the case for developing new complementary corruption indices based on hard data. This approach promises to open a new window on corruption within a particular sector, and is an opportunity to test the reliability of the more common methods for generating indices of corruption.

The Cases

The remainder of this chapter discusses seven studies that were undertaken to estimate and analyze illegal activities in Latin America's public hospitals,[6] with five of the studies explored in greater detail in the rest of the book. The seven studies were conducted in Argentina, Bolivia, Colombia, Costa Rica, Nicaragua, Peru, and Venezuela — countries whose per

---

[6] Selection of these cases was unrelated to any prior expectation of the magnitudes of corruption. Selections were made on the basis of a competitive bidding process that emphasized the best proposals, independent of country of origin.

Table 1.2 Selected Characteristics of Countries

Country	GDP per capita (1995 US$)	Health Spending per capita (1995 US$)	Share of GDP (%)
Argentina	8,112	795	9.8
Bolivia	800	48	6.0
Colombia	1,918	140	7.3
Costa Rica	2,605	224	8.6
Nicaragua	380	35	9.2
Peru	2,327	128	5.5
Venezuela	3,013	229	7.6

Source: PAHO (1998).

capita incomes range from a low of about US$400 in Nicaragua to more than US$8,000 in Argentina. The level of health spending and its share of national income also vary enormously. In Nicaragua, total health spending (both public and private) amounted to only US$35 per person in 1995, yet it represented 9.2 percent of GDP. The corresponding figures for other countries can be found in Table 1.2.

Organization of the health systems in which public hospitals operate in these countries also varies considerably. Costa Rica's health system is predominantly public and highly centralized, although in recent years it has experimented with decentralization and granted greater autonomy to some hospitals. Argentina's health system is highly fragmented, with a large share of private spending and numerous actors — including *Obras Sociales* (social and health insurance programs provided by unions for their members), national and provincial health ministries, and insurance companies.[7]

For each case study, researchers were asked to determine the major kinds of corruption, abuse, or illicit activity in public hospitals; to estimate the cost of that corruption; and to test the hypothesis that incentive struc-

---

[7] For an overview of the structure of health systems in Latin America see IDB (1996) and PAHO (1998). Further information and data about Latin American and Caribbean health systems can be found on the web at http://www.paho.org and http://www.americas.health-sector-reform.org.

tures such as ownership, accountability mechanisms, and reporting requirements influence the magnitude and scope of abuse. All of the studies used surveys of doctors, nurses, and patients to elicit perceptions of corruption in public hospitals. Several chose to focus on only a few hospitals, as in the Peruvian, Nicaraguan, and Costa Rican cases; while others canvassed a wider range of establishments — about 30 in the Venezuelan, Argentine, Bolivian, and Colombian cases. In some cases, the researchers took advantage of institutional differences between hospitals operated by ministries, social security institutes, and private entities — as in Peru and Venezuela — while others focused exclusively on public hospitals operated by the Ministry of Health. Four cases — Argentina, Venezuela, Bolivia, and Colombia — obtained data on procurement prices and analyzed them statistically.

It should be remembered that the studies, by design, focused on the kinds of illegal acts that occur within hospitals. The book does not presume that within-hospital corruption is greater or less than corruption in the health sector as a whole. Furthermore, the studies do not presume to make normative judgments about the kinds of activities that were identified. Rather the authors simply came to observe, measure, and advance our understanding of this social problem.

Public Hospitals Have Some Credibility

The general perception of corruption in public hospitals is remarkably consistent across all of the countries. Whenever respondents were asked about the degree of corruption in public hospitals, or the health sector, compared to other institutions in society, public health services were rated relatively well. In Costa Rica patients, doctors, and nurses rated the Ministry of Health and the Costa Rican Social Security Board as among the least corrupt institutions in society — ranking the Presidency and traffic police as the most corrupt. This finding was echoed in Bolivia, where the hospitals were seen as least corrupt (along with the Church and schools) and the police as the most corrupt. In Argentina, as well, only a minority affirmed that public hospitals were the most corrupt institution in the public sector.

Another common result was that patients always had a more favorable perspective of the health system than did doctors, who in turn had a more favorable perception than nurses. When asked to rank the Costa Rican Social Security Board on a scale of 1 to 10 (10 being the most corrupt), patients in Costa Rica gave it an average score of 6.1, compared to averages of 6.8 by doctors and 7.6 by nurses. In Bolivia only 39 percent of surveyed patients considered corruption to be "very frequent" in public hospitals, compared to 55 percent and 60 percent of surveyed doctors and nurses, respectively. Similarly, in Argentina 24 percent of doctors thought corruption was greater in public hospitals than in the rest of society, while 35 percent of nurses agreed.

Common Abuses

Overall, the studies demonstrated concerns about a wide range of illicit practices. These included theft of medical supplies, absenteeism by doctors and nurses, illegal payments for services, excessive payments for inputs and contracted services, favoritism in appointments and promotions, unauthorized use of public facilities for private medical practice, unnecessary referrals to private consultations, and inducement of unnecessary medical interventions.

Although all these problems were ubiquitous, their incidence and relative importance varied significantly among the different studies. In Argentina, Venezuela, and Colombia, the main focuses of concern were bribes and graft associated with service contracts and procurement. Theft was rated as a significant problem in Bolivia, Costa Rica, Peru, and Venezuela. Referrals of patients to private practice were identified in most of the cases, but only in Bolivia was it ranked as a major abuse. In Bolivia and Argentina, illegal payments for improved service were highlighted; and absenteeism was considered a serious issue in Argentina, Venezuela, Colombia, and Costa Rica.

Based on these initial findings, each case then chose a few of the most serious problems to examine in depth. Table 1.3 summarizes which forms of illicit activity were analyzed in each case, and also indicates which ones were analyzed statistically.

Stealing Medical Supplies

Theft of medical supplies was rated as extremely common in Venezuela and Costa Rica. In Venezuela, even casual observation demonstrates how this can impact the service quality of public hospitals — patients' families fre-

Table 1.3 Illegal Activities and Statistical Methods by Country

	Venezuela	Argentina	Bolivia	Peru	Colombia	Costa Rica	Nicaragua
Theft	✔ model		✔			✔	✔
Absenteeism	✔ model	✔		✔		✔	✔
Illegal fees			✔ model			✔	✔
Overpayment for supplies	✔ model	✔ model	✔ model		✔ model		
Excessive Cesareans				✔ model			

Notes: A checkmark indicates that the problem was identified as serious in that country's hospitals. "Model" indicates that the problem was analyzed econometrically.

quently must obtain medical supplies at their own expense. Fully two-thirds of surveyed hospital personnel knew of cases in which medical supplies were stolen, and 64 percent knew about theft of medications. On average, medical personnel estimated between 10 percent and 13 percent of all medications and supplies were stolen.

In Costa Rica, 71 percent of the doctors and 83 percent of the nurses reported that equipment or materials had been stolen in their hospital. Nurses thought this was much more common than did doctors. About 80 percent of the nurses considered theft to be "a lot" or "some"[8], while a significant portion of doctors considered theft to be only occasional.

Stealing Time

Absenteeism is a common problem that compromises the quality and timeliness of medical services. Research in Venezuela estimated that specialists and senior doctors missed about one-third of their contracted service hours, while residents and nurses were absent about 13 percent and 7 percent of the time, respectively. In Peru, doctors and nurses had concurring views about absenteeism among public hospital staff. About 12 percent thought it was very common, and nearly 20 percent considered it to be "common" (ha-

---

[8] Editor's note: The categories were *mucho*, *regular*, and *poca*, translated here as "a lot," "some," and "little," respectively.

bitual). Nevertheless divergence appeared when estimating absenteeism among doctors, specifically. Nurses thought that doctors were absent much more than did the doctors themselves. Interestingly the reported level of absenteeism was only insignificant in one of the four Peruvian hospitals for which data was collected — the private one. Even in Costa Rica, which generally is viewed as having one of the best health systems in Latin America, high levels of absenteeism were reported. Some 65 percent of the doctors and 87 percent of the nurses indicated that physicians were unjustifiably absent from work. And of this subsample, more than 80 percent indicated such absences were "daily" or "once or twice per week."

Even when doctors are not technically absent, they may be seeing private patients on public time in public facilities, in effect double billing for their services. Doctors in Costa Rica estimated that about one-fifth of their colleagues committed such acts, while nurses thought that fully half of all doctors did so. Of these respondents, more than half affirmed that such unauthorized use occurred daily or at least once per week.

Curiously, key informants talked about absenteeism being a problem in Colombia and Argentina, but the surveys there indicated relatively modest amounts of lost work time. In Colombia, for example, it was estimated that doctors were absent about 5 percent of the time for which they were contracted. This apparent contradiction indicates that either key informants (largely hospital directors and chiefs of staff) overstated the problem in interviews, or the surveys seriously underestimated the amount of absenteeism. Despite its relatively low rate of absenteeism, the Colombian study quantified the cost of such absenteeism in the hospitals of Bogota — and it came to over US$1 million a year.

Charging for Free Services

It has been a central tenet of many Latin American public health systems, and a right that is frequently enshrined in the national Constitution, that public health services should be provided free of charge. For a variety of reasons, this is not so in practice. Sometimes charges are "necessary" to purchase materials that are lacking in hospital stores; sometimes illegal fees are charged by hospitals to complement low staff incomes and retain staff (or give them incentives to show up for work). In some contexts, it is also difficult to distinguish between "tips"— tokens of gratitude and reciprocity that may be culturally expected — and fees imposed as a *quid pro quo*. This blurring between graft and gift is particularly noted in the study of Bolivia, where rural "fees" are often paid in kind (e.g., chickens).

Despite these qualifications, most fees paid for public health services are illegal charges; and whatever their object or use, they lack the most basic transparency necessary to protect patients. In Bolivia the government's National Maternal and Child Insurance program is supposed to provide free basic maternal and child health services to the population. Yet the Bolivian study found that 40 percent of surveyed patients indicated having paid fees for such services. The average payment was Bs 40 (about US$6.60). Ironically, despite this payment of illicit fees, two-thirds of patients thought public hospitals were less or equally prone to corruption than other institutions in society. Either the fees were genuinely considered expressions of gratitude, or it may reflect a worrisome acceptance of petty graft.

Illicit fees are not confined to Bolivia. The study in Costa Rica also provided convincing evidence that such payments are quite common. More than 85 percent of doctors and nurses stated that they knew of cases in which physicians unjustifiably charged patients. In fact, half of the Costa Rican patients affirmed having made payments as high as US$35 for a medical service in a public establishment — close to the average price of a private-sector consultation.

Overpayment: Incompetence or Theft?

Four of the cases — Argentina, Bolivia, Colombia, and Venezuela — collected information from hospital records on specific homogeneous medical supplies or medications. Despite the best efforts by national offices to negotiate standard prices or set price ceilings, the variation across hospitals is dramatic. These differences could not be explained by quality, quantity, credit terms, purchase date, hospital size, or expiration date. Instead the record demonstrates considerable wastage in procurement that can only be attributed to gross mismanagement or corruption. The ratio of highest-to-lowest purchase price for saline solution, cotton, sugar solutions, and penicillin ranged from as little as 3:1, to as much as 36:1 in the case of prices paid for cotton in Bolivia (see Figure 1.2).

The net impact of excessive prices on public budgets could be enormous. In Bogota, Colombia, the overpayments for seven specific medica-

Figure 1.2 Medical Supply Price Differences across Hospitals in Four Countries

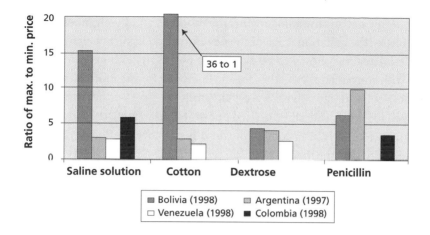

tions and supplies were estimated to total more than US$2 million per year — enough to cover medical services for an additional 24,000 people. A recent study in Guatemala estimated that a new policy eliminating centralized purchasing by the health ministry yielded savings of almost 50 percent. This made it possible to extend basic health care to 3.5 million people who had previously lacked access to any medical services (Nieves et al., 2000).

Risking Mothers' Health

Only one study, in Peru, sought to test whether doctors carried out unnecessary, and potentially risky, medical interventions. It did so by analyzing data on births by Cesarean section. It found that Cesarean deliveries accounted for 21 percent and 29 percent of all births in two health ministry hospitals. In a Social Security Institute hospital and a private clinic the shares skyrocketed to as high as 59 percent and 78 percent of all deliveries, respectively. The excessively high Cesarean rates are puzzling, but the distribution is even more so. Medical research indicates that the share of medically required Cesarean sections is considerably below 10 percent. Furthermore, one would expect higher shares of Cesareans among higher-risk populations — women with more children, from lower socioeconomic backgrounds, with less education, and with less prenatal care. Yet it is the Social Security Institute and private clinic, with patients from higher socioeconomic classes, in which Cesarean surgeries are most common.

After statistically adjusting for the mother's age, the number of previous births, the gestational age of the newborn, and its birthweight, the ratio of Cesareans was shown to be associated positively with expected income and with convenience (whether for the doctor or for the mother is unclear). In particular, doctors who were paid under fee-for-service contracts or worked for the private clinic carried out more Cesareans than those on fixed contracts. Similarly, after controlling for other factors, the doctors who could more easily control their schedules, those in the Social Security Institute, were found to schedule more Cesarean surgeries prior to holidays and weekends.

Does It Pay to Be Honest?

Generally people who enter the medical profession are expected to be socially motivated, to be guided by a desire to serve others — and those entering the public sector presumably do so out of a desire to serve people least able to access needed medical care. Why, then, is there so much evidence of misuse of public facilities, absenteeism, and theft?

After documenting the kinds and magnitudes of corruption, the studies explore a variety of avenues to pin down those aspects of hospital management, ownership, or contractual arrangement that might encourage or discourage illegal activities. In doing this, the studies depart from the assumption that behavior is governed by idealistic service providers, and follow the rational-choice literature. Under this set of assumptions, bureaucratic behavior is rational in the sense that agents weigh the costs and benefits of dishonesty before acting and then take the action that gives them maximum expected utility.

Following Becker and Stigler (1974), one posits a decision-making process in which the individual bureaucrat weighs the opportunity to misbehave. If these individuals are honest, then they behave correctly (from the principal's point of view), receive their pay, and gain satisfaction from a job honestly and well done (w). If, instead, they choose to steal supplies, be absent, or take bribes, then they face a lottery. With some probability (q), they are detected and fired. This means they must pay a penalty (P), which may include moral costs, but can earn an alternative wage (w^0), which is what the private sector or the informal sector will pay them. In the complementary probability $(1 - q)$, the bureaucrat will escape detection and earn his or her salary (w) and the value of the illicit act (B). The condition ensuring bureaucratic honesty is described, as follows:

$$w > \theta\left(w^0 - P\right) + \left(1 - \theta\right)\left(w + B\right) \qquad [1.1]$$

This formulation is useful because it allows one to classify into systematic and meaningful categories different mechanisms for influencing the level of corruption. The following conditions will generate incentives to be more honest:

- Wages in the public sector relative to the private sector are higher $(w - w^0)$;

- The probability of detection is higher (q);

- Penalties for dishonesty are higher (P); and

- Potential gains are lower (B).

Note that the prestige accorded a public servant is quite important since it is a relatively "cheap" way of providing a benefit without increasing salaries (i.e., a sum added to w). It is also interesting to reflect on the role played by the probability of detection (q). If q is small, then no wage or penalty, however high, can affect the bureaucrat's decision to be corrupt. In the limit, if detection is impossible, then $q = 0$, reducing the equation as follows:

$$w > w + B \qquad [1.2]$$

In this case, bureaucrats would always be corrupt because the value, shown on the right-hand side of the equation, will always be large, and the incentive to cheat will be very strong. One hopes that individuals are moral beings who abhor corrupt behavior, whether or not the deeds could be discovered, and that this aversion outweighs the attraction of B. In such a case, corruption would not occur. However, the extent of corrupt practices attests to the risks of basing policy on such hopes, even in sectors such as health in which social motivation is presumably quite high. Hence, some positive probability of detecting abuses is a necessary element of public policy.

Many factors affect this probability of detection (q). If inputs and outputs are easily measured, detection is easier. When comparisons with other individuals or agents are available, as in procurement outlays, it becomes easier to detect the overpayments that may signal corruption. Thus mechanisms to collect and process information are obviously key. And if those mechanisms are to work, the people collecting and analyzing the information must have incentives to act upon the problems they uncover. For this reason, systems with a variety of monitoring and supervisory mechanisms are likely to be more successful at reducing corruption. In health services, one can do this by creating channels for communication and action by local health boards, patients, community members, and regional authorities.

The penalty associated with being "caught" has two categories: the penalty itself (fines, jail) and loss of income (when w exceeds w^0). Penalties in many countries are weak because judicial processes are slow. Penalties will also be less effective if there is a history of impunity or light sentences. Efficiency wages — earnings higher than the individual could expect in the event of being fired — can be a strong disincentive to cheat, but it requires a credible threat that detection will lead to dismissal.

Restricting the individual's discretion at work and scope of activity can discourage potential gains from illegal acts. A manager with a small budget, few materials, and little power to appoint and fire staff has less opportunity for ill-gotten gains than one with large financial flows, expenditures, and control over staff appointments. The trade-off here is that reducing discretion too severely can be self-defeating if it means being unable to efficiently provide services mandated by public policy or to respond creatively to heterogeneous needs. Hence, well-organized systems tend to delegate as much responsibility as possible within the constraints given by the capacity to monitor and supervise the actions of subordinates.

The analysis provided in the case studies justifies some preliminary claims about the major factors encouraging or discouraging illegal activities.

First, there was *little evidence that higher wages for procurement officers were associated with less corruption.* In Argentina, a corruption index based on procurement prices was analyzed, using the procurement officer's salary as one explanatory factor.[9] The coefficient was insignificant. In Colombia, a similar procedure found that the procurement officer's salary was negatively associated with prices paid overall (i.e., including both competitive and direct purchases). However the salary had a *positive* association with prices when analyzing only direct purchases — over which the procurement officer has the most discretion and the least oversight. In Venezuela, a similar analysis found that higher wages were associated with *higher* levels of corruption. The authors of that study believe that this surprising finding confirms opinions expressed among key informants that corrupt individuals bribe their way into jobs that provide opportunities for illicit gain. The high salary is simply another aspect of the corruption, which combines appointments, pay, and graft. This contradicts other studies' findings that average pay in the public sector as a whole is inversely related to aggregate corruption (e.g., Van Rijckeghem and Weder, 1997).

The Argentine study goes even further and suggests that *impunity may be the principal factor contributing to corruption in public hospitals*. When Argentina experimented with publishing procurement price information, and thereby increased the risk of detection, procurement prices dropped dramatically — even before the first dissemination of this information. Yet six months later the wide range of procurement prices had reappeared — presumably because the procurement officers saw that, in practice, the price information was not being used to penalize or sanction anyone. Impunity turns detection of crimes into a worthless deterrent.[10]

The Venezuelan study also demonstrates that low probabilities of detection and penalty are associated with higher procurement prices. The perverse relationship with wages now seems less surprising. As noted earlier, no wage is sufficient to insure honesty if the probability of detection and sanction is null.

This finding in the Venezuelan analysis of theft was confirmed in a comparable analysis of absenteeism. For doctors, the low probability of capture and the potential degree of penalty appeared to have a significant im-

---

[9] To be precise, the variable was the *efficiency wage*, i.e., the difference between the officer's current salary and his or her expected salary in alternative employment in the labor market. See the Argentina chapter of this volume.

[10] This brings to mind the famous statement by Ademar de Barros when running for Governor in São Paulo during the 1950s. His campaign slogan was, *Roubo mas faz* (I steal but I get things done). So much for transparency.

pact on absenteeism. Among nurses, however, only the probability of sanction was significant, not the size of the penalty.

In Bogota, Colombia, researchers were able to distinguish doctors who had "permanent" contracts under the civil service code, which grants them substantial job stability, from those who are "contracted" under the normal private labor law code, which makes discipline or dismissal by employers easier. The substantially higher rate of absenteeism among the permanent doctors underlines the conclusion that the credibility of detection leading to sanction is a critical factor in discouraging corruption.

Survey findings in Peru are also consistent with this emphasis on the importance of detection and sanction. Among sample respondents, more than half of the doctors attributed absenteeism to the potential earnings that a practitioner could receive from working elsewhere during contracted hours. But a substantial portion also indicated that low probability of detection and sanction was a significant factor (about one-fifth).

The study on Bolivia in chapter 2 helps to refine this focus on detection and sanction. Its authors distinguish two forms of accountability — voice/exit and hierarchical control. The first form refers to mechanisms that allow clients or patients (a) to provide meaningful feedback to service providers and have some expectation of response (voice), or (b) to penalize providers by taking their "business" elsewhere (exit). The second category, hierarchical controls, refers to formal mechanisms of monitoring and supervision within the particular vertical organization of a service.

In Bolivia, the Law of Popular Participation transferred responsibility for hospitals to municipalities and created local hospital boards — with community members — to oversee and manage them. At the same time, the national government continued to transfer resources and monitor hospital expenditures. Gray-Molina and his colleagues demonstrate that both forms of accountability have a statistically significant impact on reducing illegal fees and overpayment for supplies and medications. Given the dispersed nature of these hospitals, it is perhaps unsurprising that the voice mechanisms — indicated by the presence and activity of a local hospital board — had a more robust impact than the hierarchical controls, which were measured by whether or not hiring is competitive and whether or not staff are supervised.

In Colombia, however, researchers found that the only factor statistically correlated with lower procurement prices was the existence of accounting controls for supplies and the perception, by medical personnel, that effective supervision existed. By contrast, the measures of discretion and autonomy (such as share of doctors on temporary contracts or activity of the hospital board) were unimportant. This suggests that if discretion is important, it clearly requires accountability to be effective.

Using Hard and Soft Indices to Clarify the Picture

One goal of these studies was to demonstrate that objective data on corruption can be usefully collected and analyzed. Given that procurement price information has proven to be quite effective in analyzing the correlates of corruption, how do "hard" indicators stack up against the more commonly used "soft" indicators?

Only the Bolivian study explicitly analyzed the relationship between the levels of illegal activity as measured by excessive procurement prices and levels measured by opinion surveys. However, the researchers found a significant and positive correlation between the level of procurement prices and the ranking of hospital corruption levels by respondents. The correlation coefficient was 0.55, with strong statistical significance. Although drawn from only one study, this finding offers some corroboration for subjective indices, suggesting they are reliable, if noisy, indicators of corruption. More-objective measures — such as those developed in this book — need not and likely will not displace opinion survey indices. Instead, the new indicators should provide more tools to penetrate the surface noise and analyze a phenomenon that is largely hidden.

Summary

No society, government, or public service is completely crime-free. Yet we know that some do a better job of controlling illicit activities than others. At the beginning of this new century, fighting corruption has entered the public debate in Latin America. If this opportunity is to be seized, politicians and policymakers must have access to the information they need in order to focus attention on the grossest violations of the public trust and design policies and mechanisms that will discourage corrupt behavior. This challenge is essential for public hospitals, and the health sector more generally, because these facilities manage large amounts of public resources, provide public services that are of critical importance, and play a significant role in sustaining confidence in public institutions.

The studies in this volume offer recommendations relevant to tackling abuses in public hospitals, but also abuses in other areas of public policy. They suggest that:

- Raising salaries may not deter corruption in the absence of credible sanctions;

- Raising the probability of detection is probably the most powerful instrument available for reducing corruption in public hospitals as long as there are some associated consequences;

- Detection and penalization can be strengthened not only through hierarchical controls, but also by mechanisms of voice and exit (e.g., local hospital boards and competition); and

- Ownership, payment mechanisms, and other institutionalized incentives do influence the degree of illicit activity.

The case studies in the following chapters are not the end of the story. Rather they are a beginning. They demonstrate that the challenge of confronting corruption can be faced under difficult and dangerous circumstances, that objective information can be used to corroborate and confirm survey-based perceptions, and that analysis can yield policy recommendations on which governments should act. Certainly, it is impossible to leave things as they are because the stakes are too high.

CHAPTER 2

Does Voice Matter? Participation and Controlling Corruption in Bolivian Hospitals

George Gray-Molina, Ernesto Pérez de Rada,
and Ernesto Yañez

In Bolivia, the Law of Popular Participation transferred responsibility for hospitals to municipalities and created local boards — with community members — to oversee and manage hospitals. At the same time, the national government continued to transfer resources and monitor hospital expenditures. In this chapter, the authors demonstrate that both forms of accountability have a statistically significant impact on reducing illegal fees and overpayment for supplies and medications. The voice mechanisms, indicated by the presence and activity of a local hospital board, had a more robust and larger impact than the hierarchical controls, measured by whether or not hiring is competitive and whether or not staff are supervised.

Introduction

The scope and determinants of corruption have been poorly studied in Bolivia. Although public theft, patronage, clientelism, and nepotism have been routinely denounced in government policy statements and cited in international donor reports, little hard evidence has shown the costs or effects of corrupt public practices. The recent wave of state reforms that has swept through the region suggests the importance of "getting institutions right" by changing the way in which public policy is designed, implemented, and monitored (Burki and Perry, 1998; Graham and Naim, 1998; Picciotto and Wiesner, 1998). In Bolivia, reformers have placed decentralization and citizen participation at the heart of the policy reform agenda (Burki, Perry et al., 1998; Peterson, 1997; Campbell, 1997). During the past five years, the framework for social service delivery has been radically overhauled to amplify citizens' voice and heighten public accountability. Despite these ambitious efforts, public-sector performance is still perceived to be widely heterogeneous and subject to particularistic interests (Gray-Molina and Molina, 1997; Gray-Molina, 1997). What accounts for this spotty record of "success" and "failure" observed in the field?

This chapter analyzes the institutional factors that affect public accountability and corruption, focusing on the incentive structure faced by providers and users of health services. The Bolivian Popular Participation and Administrative Decentralization reforms, implemented in 1994, provide a unique opportunity to compare the effects of institutional incentives versus policy performance. This study analyzes the effectiveness of hierarchical controls and voice/exit factors in deterring public corruption at the municipal level. Using data gathered from 30 municipal hospitals, the analysis surveys the Bolivian case of health service delivery, and presents a conceptual framework for analyzing corruption. It profiles typical abuses, using hard or soft data, and analyzes what determines the frequency. Results based on opinion surveys are then correlated with results from "hard" data to determine relative effectiveness. The study concludes with a brief exposition of its findings and discusses their implications for the analysis of transparency and corruption in the region.

The Health Sector and Its Context

The health sector in Bolivia accounts for significant social service expenditures, equivalent to US$284 million in 1998, or US$44 per capita, and 4.7 percent of GDP (Cárdenas and Darrás, 1997). User fees (35 percent) are the largest source of health-care financing, followed by private-sector funds (34 percent), international cooperation (14 percent), and direct government subsidies (13 percent). Expenditures are divided three ways, with 38 percent directed to private-sector services, 33 percent to social security services, and 29 percent to public-sector services. This contrasts with service coverage for the population. According to the most recent census, the largest segment relied on government coverage (44 percent, with 30 percent using public-sector providers and 14 percent using the social security system). Private coverage accounted for another 30 percent, while 24 percent reported no formal health coverage at all (INE, 1992).

Public-sector health coverage is low by regional standards and is concentrated mainly in urban areas. Mortality rates, particularly child and maternal rates, are among the highest in Latin America despite important advances in recent years. Urban/rural differentials in Bolivia continue to pose a significant challenge to increased public-sector coverage for immunization, family planning, and prenatal and postnatal care. Pneumonia, diarrhea, and other infectious and respiratory diseases account for the largest share of infant and child deaths (see Table 2.1).

Decentralization and Popular Participation

The delivery of health services in Bolivia has undergone significant changes since the Popular Participation and Administrative Decentralization reforms were implemented. The framework for providing health services now involves shared responsibility among four different public levels:

Table 2.1 Selected Health Indicators for Bolivia, by Region

	National	Urban	Rural
Public-sector coverage (%)			
Births	42	62	21
Prenatal controls	53	68	36
Family planning	18	25	7
Immunization	37	44	28
Mortality rates			
Infant (per 1,000)	75	69	106
Child (per 1,000)	116	104	162
Maternal (per 100,000)	390	274	524
Disease incidence (per 1,000 children under 5 years)			
Acute respiratory infections	19	19	17
Acute diarrheal disease	20	11	29

Sources: Instituto Nacional de Estadística (1992 and 1994).

♦ *Central government.* The Ministry of Health is the line agency charged with national policymaking in the health sector. The Ministry is responsible for designing and overseeing the implementation of medium- and long-term national health strategies. It also manages an array of national programs (for the prevention of cholera, malaria, tuberculosis, and other epidemiological diseases) funded through international cooperation and implemented by decentralized prefectural offices or private voluntary organizations. Intergovernmental transfers from the national to the local level for public health investments are administered by the Social Investment Fund, under the Ministry of the Presidency. In recent years the Health Ministry has focused almost exclusively on policy formulation (sectoral decrees and regulations) and has shifted responsibility for implementation to the prefectural and municipal levels. The central government today handles approximately 90 percent of recurrent health expenditures (primarily salaries), but only 30 percent of total public investment in the sector.

♦ *Prefectures.* The central government delegates administrative responsibilities and resources to nine prefectures. These departmental-level jurisdictions administer payroll and manage national programs designed and funded at the central level. They play an essentially passive role in policymaking and act as a hinge between municipalities and the central government.

♦ *Municipal governments.* Municipal governments have administrative and fiscal responsibility for infrastructure maintenance and equipment of first- and second-level health centers. Level I centers include community health and sanitary posts, while Level II centers are basic-service hospitals, which oversee general medical, surgical, pediatric, and gynecologic/obstetric practices. Municipalities today account for approximately 70 percent of new public investments in health infrastructure and equipment, as well as 10 percent of recurrent expenditures (mostly maintenance services).

♦ *Submunicipal institutions.* Besides the formal distribution of responsibilities and resources among the central, prefectural, and municipal levels, the Popular Participation Law provides for establishment of Local Health Directorates (DILOS) in each municipality. The DILOS is a participatory planning and monitoring board that oversees first- and second-level health centers. It is made up of three key actors: community user groups, municipal officials, and prefectural health officials. While these boards have been slow in forming, reports characterize them as being more effective than oversight committees that have been established for citizen voice, and oversight of general municipal functions (Giussani and Ruiz, 1997; Gray-Molina and O'Neill, 1998).

The introduction of intergovernmental grants for locally based programs has marked an important shift in the pattern of health service financing. The most important program is the Seguro Materno Infantil, or Maternal Infant Insurance (hereafter "Seguro"), which provides free prenatal care for women, postpartum care for mothers and infants, and basic medical care (e.g., treatment of pneumonia and diarrhea) for children under the age of six. The Seguro is financed by a required municipal contribution of 3 percent of its budget and by central government grants for personnel, supplies, and medication. Since being introduced in 1996, it has been a leader in expanding health care coverage, particularly in rural areas. A recent study (Dmytraczenko, 1998) documents increases of 70 percent in the total number of prenatal consultations, 31 percent for births attended professionally in health facilities, 266 percent in pneumonia treatments, and 86 percent in diarrhea treatments. The greatest improvements in coverage have occurred at Level I facilities (health centers) and Level II facilities (basic hospitals), administered at the municipal level (see Table 2.2).

Getting a Fix on Corruption

In a majority of cases [...] corruption ordinarily refers to the use of public office for private gain, where an official (the agent) entrusted with carrying out a task by the public (the principal) engages in some sort of malfeasance for private enrichment, which is difficult to monitor for the principal (Bardhan, 1997: 1321).

Building on Bardhan's definition, this section focuses on the types of corruption detected in the study of municipal hospitals: informal user pay-

Table 2.2 Coverage of the Maternal-Infant Insurance Program (1995–1997)

	1995	1996	1997	Increase 1995–97 (%)
Total Births	**27,622**	**28,087**	**36,362**	**31.6**
Level III General Hospitals	24,902	24,535	30,949	24.3
Level II Basic Hospitals	2,619	3,365	4,691	89.4
Level I Health Centers	101	187	432	327.7
Prenatal Visits	**61,149**	**73,390**	**104,310**	**70.6**
Level III General Hospitals	47,393	55,557	75,394	59.1
Level II Basic Hospitals	10,911	14,133	23,401	114.5
Level I Health Centers	2,845	3,700	5,515	93.8
Pneumonia (children < 6)	**1,682**	**2,446**	**6,165**	**266.5**
Level III General Hospitals	670	596	1,511	125.5
Level II Basic Hospitals	812	1,406	3,856	374.9
Level I Health Centers	200	444	798	299.0
Diarrhea (children < 6)	**13,885**	**17,657**	**25,811**	**85.9**
Level III General Hospitals	5,432	5,871	12,313	127.1
Level II Basic Hospitals	6,456	7,986	9,487	46.9
Level I Health Centers	2,006	3,800	4,011	100.0

Source: Dmytraczenko (1998).

ments, overpricing of homogeneous medical inputs, absenteeism, medical supply theft, and the private use of public facilities. It sketches out a basic analytical model to characterize the incentive structure faced by health providers and users and explain the origins of the abuse and how it can be addressed. In this model, two forms of influence over the behavior of providers can be distinguished — those that are related to hierarchical administrative controls and those related to accountability to users and the local community.

Agency Problems

The approach employed here relies on a basic principal-agent model. In such a model, the agent may do things that are not in the best interests of the principal if the two sides have different objectives and different information about the services being provided. In such a case, the agent may shirk or abuse his or her position. The principal can resort to two ways of reducing this problem, by establishing forms of monitoring and penalization and by contracts that create incentives for the agent that better induce outcomes desired by the principal (Pratt and Zeckhauser, 1985). As noted by Banerjee (1997) and Bossert (1997), the basic agency problem becomes more complex in the context of decentralized decision-making, particularly in developing countries. Decentralization policies typically expand the range of "formal" and "informal" choice in ways that elude the basic principal-agent model.

One way to capture this difference is to use the concept of decision space. According to Bossert (1977: 12),

> "Decision space" [is defined] as the range of effective choice that is allowed by the central authorities (the principal) to be utilized by local authorities (the agents). This space can be formally defined by laws and regulations. [It] defines the specific "rules of the game" for decentralized agents. The actual (or "informal") decision space may also be defined by lack of enforcement of these formal definitions that allows lower level officials to "bend the rules."

This modified principal-agent approach allows agency problems to be mapped at different levels of decision-making (prefectural, municipal, service provider) and in terms of different functions (finance, service organization, human resources) within each level. For example, while the municipal range of effective decision space for personnel hiring or firing may be limited, the decision space for the procurement of equipment may be wide. Similarly, in the case of hierarchical relations, one can note how the effective range of public oversight might be weak at the municipal level but strong at the clinic or health-post level. While decision space is sometimes likely to promote opportunities for beneficial policy innovations in local practice, in others it may actually widen the scope for corrupt, unaccountable, or arbitrary decision-making. The nature of this trade-off will become more apparent later, in analyzing particular instances of local decision-making.

Voice/Exit Problems

When local providers have some degree of autonomy and can be held accountable to those who use their services, then this user monitoring at the local level can actually make hierarchical systems of administrative control over public-service providers more effective. Some analysts have modeled this accountability-building mechanism as an issue of "voice" and "exit" (Hirschman, 1970; Paul, 1994; Picciotto, 1997). That is, users have two methods to exert pressure and provide feedback regarding their satisfaction with the public services they receive. They can communicate directly with providers through grievances, suggestions, and protests (voice), or they can withdraw their support by seeking alternatives (exit). In general, researchers have argued that public accountability is maximized when users exercise their voice option. Voice is most effective when there are no informational, legal, or institutional barriers hindering its use, and exit is unavailable. In practice, however, such constraints are prevalent in developing countries, particularly for the rural poor. How can user groups overcome these obstacles to effective monitoring of public services?

Paul (1992) considers four strategies for amplifying voice in the case of dispersed and monopolistic public-service provision for the poor: first, establishing independent monitoring groups (such as comptrollers or ombudsmen) with direct access to official sources of information and records; second, establishing participatory boards at the local government level that allow user groups to scale up the scope of their collective action; third, promoting linkages with NGOs and churches that promote external oversight mechanisms; and fourth, introducing public hearings or referenda to allow grievances to be aired openly. Bottom-up voice strategies are expected to promote public accountability by exposing agency problems related to hidden action. The "voice → accountability → performance response" model, however, is premised on the expectation that bottom-up mechanisms actually lead to top-down policy responses, which again calls into play the agency problems discussed previously. Whether or not voice is effective is ultimately an empirical question, to be assessed on a case-by-case basis.

An Analytical Model

We propose a simplified analytical model to account for the agency problems that characterize public-service delivery. While "corruption" cannot be directly observed, variations from expected service prices can be. The model approximates these variations by accounting, first, for individual and municipal-level characteristics, second, for effective administrative discretion at the municipal level (discretion in personnel hiring and management), and third, for the degree of voice exercised by service users (proxied by the degree of citizen-health-board activism). The choice to engage in corrupt public practice can be modeled in terms of the incentive structure facing potential wrongdoers. If a public official can be assumed to maximize his or her expected income, then:

$$E(Y) = (1-p)(Bc+W) + p(Cc) \tag{2.1}$$

where $E(Y)$ is expected income, Bc is the expected benefit accruing from corruption, W is wages, Cc is the expected penalty from being caught, and p is the probability of being detected.

The probability of detection can itself be modeled in terms of the institutional incentives facing the potential wrongdoer:

$$p = p(\text{Voice, Discretion}) \tag{2.2}$$

In this model, voice and administrative discretion are observed characteristics of the municipal decision-making environment. Voice deters corruption by raising the probability of detection and therefore decreasing the expected income from wrongdoing. Hierarchical controls deter corruption through two channels, both subject to agency problems. The first is backward looking, restraining the discretion with which agents operate; the second is forward looking, signaling the credibility of hierarchical controls if corrupt acts are detected.

It is hypothesized that voice is likely to be effective for practices directly involving service users (such as bribes), while hierarchical controls are likely to be important for practices relating to hidden action (such as petty theft). Voice and discretion factors are also expected to interact along a range of outcomes. In theory, four possible scenarios are relevant to our analysis (see Table 2.3). While two scenarios (high voice with narrow discretion and low voice with wide discretion) are unambiguous in their effects on accountability, the other two scenarios are likely to be of most interest because they make it possible to evaluate the differential weight of voice and hierarchical interactions.

The Evidence from Municipal Hospitals

This study uses data from a municipal hospital survey conducted in November 1998. Thirty hospitals from 24 municipalities were surveyed on in-

Table 2.3 Hypotheses for Outcomes Based on Voice and Discretion

| | Voice | |
	Weak	**Strong**
Administrative discretion:		
	+/– Accountability	**+ Accountability**
Narrow	Depends on agency incentives: "Passive" service provider "Passive" service user	Strong top-down and bottom-up incentives for public accountability
	– Accountability	**+/– Accountability**
Wide	Weak top-down and bottom-up incentives for public accountability	Depends on agency incentives: "Activist" service provider "Activist" service user

formal payments, input pricing, and perceptions of absenteeism, supply and equipment theft, and inappropriate use of public facilities.[1] The sample was selected in two steps: First, municipalities were ranked according to an index of administrative discretion, as reported by the 1997 Census of Municipal Governments. "Highly" discretionary systems were defined by the absence of (1) a competitive hiring system, (2) an investment planning system, and (3) an internal auditing system. "Low" discretionary municipalities were defined by the presence of one or more of these indices. Second, 12 "highly" discretionary municipalities and 12 "low" discretionary municipalities were selected for canvassing from three clusters of municipalities located around the cities of La Paz, Cochabamba, and Santa Cruz. The final sample included 30 municipal hospitals. Twenty-eight of the hospitals surveyed were Level II municipal hospitals charged with four areas of health care: general medicine, surgery, pediatrics, and gynecology. Two hospitals were Level III, charged with more-specialized services (see Table 2.4 for general characteristics of the sample).

---

[1] The survey was conducted by Encuestas y Estudios, an affiliate of Gallup Polls in Bolivia.

Table 2.4 Characteristics of Level II Basic-Service Hospitals in Bolivia

	Level II hospitals	Available beds	Doctors	Nurses	Admin. personnel
Universe	188	2,985	434	689	433
Sample	30	853	220	405	173
El Alto	1	52	18	14	12
Achacachi	1	15	5	8	8
Patacamaya	1	4	3	11	1
Viacha	1	30	4	20	3
Montero	1	56	9	20	8
Punata	1	32	9	11	14
Quillacollo	1	27	7	10	7
Capinota	1	22	5	6	4
Sipe Sipe	1	16	2	7	1
Tiquipaya	1	12	1	2	0
Copacabana	1	12	2	4	2
Pucarani	1	9	3	10	4
Sacaba	1	6	4	4	3
Ayo Ayo	1	10	1	0	2
Mineros	1	6	3	11	7
Batallas	1	12	3	5	2
San Carlos	1	47	5	11	7
El Torno	1	14	1	6	1
Yapacani	1	3	1	0	0
Coloca	1	18	4	5	3
Buena Vista	1	12	3	7	2
La Paz*	3	189	57	72	32
Cochabamba*	3	96	32	81	24
Santa Cruz	3	153	38	60	26

Sources: Censo Municipal, Ministerio de Desarrollo Sostenible y Planificación y Ministerio de Hacienda (1999); Secretaria Nacional de Salud – DOSSME (1997).

Note. In La Paz and Cochabamba, one Level III (general services) hospital was also sampled along with two Level II (basic services) hospitals.

Although the sample covers only about a sixth of all Level II hospitals, it accounts for nearly two-thirds of the nurses, half of the doctors, and a third of the bed capacity of basic-service hospitals in the country.

Survey data for the sample hospitals was collected from four different sources: patients (301 observations), nurses (60 observations), doctors (55 observations), and hospital administrators (24 observations). Administrative and citizen participation data from the 1998 Municipal Census was also used to construct explanatory variables on voice/exit and hierarchical controls.

Perceptions of Corruption

Three types of perceptions about corruption were collected. First, patients, doctors, and nurses were asked to assess various health and nonhealth sector institutions on a continuum from least to most corrupt. From this data, including patients' assessment of their own workplace, the performance of an array of public- and private-sector institutions can be compared. Second, the same groups were asked to assess an array of corrupt practices, most of which deal with health services. Finally, doctors and nurses were asked to assess the frequency of corrupt practices within their own workplaces. This included an evaluation of absenteeism, theft, and the misuse of public facilities for private gain. To gauge whether incidence was rising, falling, or stable, patients, doctors, and nurses were asked to compare between past and present corruption in the health sector.

Findings for health- and nonhealth-sector comparisons by patients, nurses, and doctors are reported in Table 2.5. A general pattern emerges for comparisons across groups: The police and customs are perceived to be the most corrupt institutions, while the Church, public schools, and public hospitals are seen as the least corrupt. On a scale moving from 1 (never corrupt) to 5 (always corrupt), patients score Church-related corruption at 1.83, public school corruption at 2.62, and public hospital corruption at 2.63.

Breaking down comparisons by group, patients see the police and customs as being most corrupt and the Church and public hospitals as least corrupt. Doctors, on the other hand, see police, customs, and the Presidency as being more corrupt than patients do. The Ministry of Health is scored 2.64 by nurses, 2.84 by patients, and 3.48 by doctors. The ministry is judged to be "always" corrupt by 18 percent of doctors, 17 percent of nurses, and 6 percent of patients, with the largest subsamples of respondents (25 percent

Table 2.5 Perceived Frequency of Corruption in Bolivian Institutions (In percent)

"How frequent is corruption in . . . ?"	Never	A little	Some	A lot	Always	No reply	Total	Average score
According to patients:								
Presidency	1.7	4.7	10.3	33.9	24.6	24.9	100	4.00
Customs	1.0	3.7	9.0	29.6	38.9	17.9	100	4.24
Supreme Court	3.3	7.0	9.6	25.3	25.3	29.6	100	3.88
Municipal government	2.7	6.3	16.9	31.2	28.6	14.3	100	3.89
Public utilities	7.0	17.9	19.9	15.0	8.6	31.6	100	3.00
Public schools	14.6	19.6	32.9	11.0	3.3	18.6	100	2.62
Police	1.7	3.0	11.0	24.3	47.8	12.3	100	4.29
Catholic Church	38.6	15.3	12.0	5.7	1.0	27.6	100	1.83
Ministry of Health	10.0	17.9	24.6	14.3	6.0	27.2	100	2.84
Public hospitals	15.3	25.6	19.9	11.6	7.3	20.3	100	2.63
According to doctors:								
Presidency	7.3	1.8	7.3	29.1	40.0	14.6	100	4.08
Customs	0.0	0.0	1.8	32.7	58.2	7.3	100	4.60
Supreme Court	1.8	3.6	21.8	34.6	30.9	7.3	100	3.96
Municipal government	0.0	5.5	12.7	38.2	40.0	3.6	100	4.17
Public utilities	5.5	14.6	25.5	18.2	18.2	18.2	100	3.35
Public schools	20.0	21.8	30.9	5.5	7.3	14.6	100	2.51
Police	1.8	3.6	7.3	21.8	61.8	3.6	100	4.43
Catholic Church	38.2	21.8	18.2	1.8	1.8	18.2	100	1.86
Ministry of Health	3.6	9.1	34.6	21.8	18.2	12.7	100	3.48
Public hospitals	9.1	30.9	36.4	16.4	1.8	5.5	100	2.69
According to nurses:								
Presidency	0.0	0.0	13.3	30.0	33.3	23.3	100	4.26
Customs	3.3	0.0	6.7	23.3	50.0	16.7	100	4.40
Supreme Court	0.0	3.3	16.7	26.7	30.0	23.3	100	4.09
Municipal government	0.0	3.3	23.3	20.0	46.7	6.7	100	3.48
Public utilities	6.7	13.3	30.0	6.7	16.7	26.7	100	3.18
Public schools	20.0	20.0	23.3	10.0	3.3	23.3	100	2.43
Police	6.7	0.0	6.7	20.0	50.0	16.7	100	4.28
Catholic Church	53.3	16.7	3.3	3.3	0.0	23.3	100	1.43
Ministry of Health	23.3	13.3	23.3	16.7	6.7	16.7	100	2.64
Public hospitals	16.7	23.3	33.3	13.3	13.3	0.0	100	2.83

Source: Municipal Hospital Survey (Encuestas y Estudios, 1998).

Notes: Percentages may not sum to 100 due to rounding. The "Average Score" is a weighted average, where 1 = "never," 2 = "a little," 3 = "some," 4 = "a lot," 5 = "always," and "no reply" is excluded.

of patients, 35 percent of doctors, and 23 percent of nurses) rating the ministry as being "sometimes" corrupt. Given the context of Bolivia, perception of municipal government performance is especially relevant. Municipal governments were scored 4.17 by doctors, 3.89 by patients, and 3.48 by nurses, with approximately 29 percent of patients, 40 percent of doctors, and 47 percent of nurses rating it "always" corrupt, painting a relatively dismal picture in the wake of decentralization reforms.

Respondents were also asked to rate the frequency of corrupt practices within the public sector (see Table 2.6). Bribes related to red-tape paperwork were seen to be most frequent (with average scores of 4.26 from doctors, 4.24 from nurses, and 3.91 from patients), followed by public works

Table 2.6 Perceived Incidence of Corrupt Practices in the Public Sector (In percent)

"How frequent are the following acts?"	Never	A little	Some	A lot	Always	No reply	Total	Average score
According to patients:								
Bribes (paperwork)	1.3	5.6	18.3	33.6	26.3	15.0	100	3.91
Municipal public works	2.0	6.0	20.9	26.3	20.3	24.6	100	3.75
Municipal theft	2.3	8.3	21.6	24.3	20.9	22.6	100	3.68
Municipal absenteeism	4.7	12.0	23.9	17.9	9.6	31.9	100	3.23
Bribes (hospitals)	16.3	20.3	20.9	17.3	6.0	19.3	100	2.71
According to doctors:								
Bribes (paperwork)	0.0	1.8	14.6	38.2	43.6	1.8	100	4.26
Municipal public works	1.8	5.5	18.2	30.9	36.4	7.3	100	4.02
Municipal theft	0.0	14.6	14.6	27.3	25.5	18.2	100	3.77
Municipal absenteeism	3.6	12.7	34.6	23.6	9.1	16.4	100	3.26
Bribes (hospitals)	25.5	21.8	21.8	18.2	7.3	5.5	100	2.57
According to nurses:								
Bribes (paperwork)	0.0	6.7	0.0	43.3	33.3	16.7	100	4.24
Municipal public works	0.0	6.7	16.7	26.7	30.0	20.0	100	4.00
Municipal theft	0.0	6.7	16.7	33.3	16.7	26.7	100	3.82
Municipal absenteeism	6.7	33.3	10.0	23.3	13.3	13.3	100	3.04
Bribes (hospitals)	40.0	16.7	3.3	20.0	3.3	16.7	100	2.16

Source: Municipal Hospital Survey (Encuestas y Estudios, 1998).

Notes: Percentages may not sum to 100 due to rounding. The "Average Score" is a weighted average, where 1 = "never," 2 = "a little," 3 = "some," 4 = "a lot," 5 = "always," and "no reply" is excluded.

corruption (scored 4.02, 4.00, and 3.75, respectively) and municipal theft of supplies and equipment (scored 3.77, 3.82, and 3.68, respectively). Doctors are generally more critical than are patients of public-sector corruption. Forty-four percent of doctors say red-tape bribes "always" happen, compared to 33 percent of nurses and 26 percent of patients. In addition, 36 percent of doctors say public works corruption "always" occurs, compared to 30 percent of nurses and 20 percent of patients. The least-frequent corrupt actions according to respondents are hospital bribes (scored 2.57 by doctors, 2.16 by nurses, and 2.71 by patients) and municipal absenteeism (scored 3.26, 3.04, and 3.23, respectively). The highest rates of "no reply" come from patients (32 percent for municipal absenteeism, 25 percent for public works corruption) and nurses (27 percent for municipal theft).

Table 2.7 Perceptions of Incidence of Corrupt Practices in Public Hospitals (In percent)

How frequent are the following acts?	Never	A little	Some	A lot	Always	No reply	Total	Average score
According to doctors:								
Procurement:								
cleaning	5	9	18	9	40	19	100	3.84
construction	7	13	18	11	7	24	100	3.50
catering	9	7	22	11	31	20	100	3.59
supplies	9	16	22	13	20	20	100	3.22
Scheduling procedures	0	5	15	16	49	15	100	4.27
Patient misreferral	2	9	11	27	38	13	100	4.04
Theft of supplies	2	9	7	13	44	25	100	4.17
According to nurses:								
Procurement:								
cleaning	16	7	7	3	37	30	100	3.52
construction	7	10	7	23	23	30	100	3.66
catering	7	7	17	7	33	30	100	3.76
supplies	17	7	13	7	13	43	100	2.88
Scheduling procedures	7	7	3	7	40	37	100	4.05
Patient misreferral	7	0	13	13	47	20	100	4.17
Theft of supplies	3	7	7	17	50	17	100	4.44

Source: Municipal Hospital Survey (Encuestas y Estudios, 1998).

Notes: Percentages may not sum to 100 due to rounding. The "Average Score" is a weighted average, where 1 = "never," 2 = "a little," 3 = "some," 4 = "a lot," 5 = "always," and "no reply" is excluded.

Doctors and nurses were also asked to assess the frequency of corrupt acts within their workplaces (see Table 2.7). The most frequent practices identified by both groups were theft of hospital supplies, referral of patients to a private practice, and payments for scheduling medical procedures. Doctors gave scheduling of procedures a score of 4.27, followed by 4.17 for supply theft and 4.04 for patient misreferral. Forty-nine percent of doctors believe payments for scheduling procedures "always" occurs, followed by 44 percent who similarly rank supply theft. Doctors see medical supply procurement as being least corrupt (scoring it 3.22). Nurses, on the other hand, see supply theft as most frequent (scoring it 4.44), followed by misreferral of patients to private practice (scored 4.16). Nurses see medical supply procurement as being least corrupt (scored 2.88), followed by cleaning service procurement (scored 3.52). The highest rates of "no reply" for doctors concerned questions of supply theft (25 percent) and construction procurement (24 percent), and for nurses, questions of supply procurement (43 percent) and scheduling of procedures (37 percent).

Finally, respondents were asked to assess how health sector corruption compares to corruption in other social institutions and whether it has increased over the past five years, following the implementation of decentralization reforms (see Table 2.8). Half of the patients responded that health sector corruption is less frequent than elsewhere in society. Forty-two percent also believe the frequency has declined. When asked whether health sector corruption was greater or smaller than corruption in their own workplace, the largest group of patients (44 percent) chose not to answer. Nearly two-thirds of the doctors thought that health sector corruption is overwhelmingly less frequent than in other parts of society, and they are evenly divided on whether corruption has increased or decreased during the past five years. Approximately 7 percent thought the health sector had no corruption at all. Nurses are even more optimistic. Close to 73 percent say that health sector corruption is less frequent than in other social institutions. The largest subsample of nurses (37 percent) thought that health sector corruption had decreased in the past five years.

The perceptions reviewed in this section portray a comparatively benign picture of corruption in the health sector. Most respondents suggest that the health sector is one of the three least corrupt from a list of ten other public and private institutions. When asked to assess the frequency of corrupt acts in the public sector, most respondents identify red-tape-related

Table 2.8 Comparing Health Sector Corruption to Other Sectors and over Time (In percent)

How do you assess health sector corruption today compared to . . . ?	Greater	Same	Less	No corruption	No response	Total
According to patients:						
Other social institutions	4.0	21.6	50.2	0.0	24.3	100
Your workplace	5.9	17.7	32.9	0.0	43.5	100
Five years ago	13.6	22.6	41.5	0.0	22.3	100
According to doctors:						
Other social institutions	23.6	1.8	63.6	7.3	3.6	100
Five years ago	36.4	20.0	34.6	5.5	3.6	100
According to nurses:						
Other social institutions	0.0	6.7	73.3	13.3	6.7	100
Five years ago	16.7	23.3	36.7	10.0	13.3	100

Source: Municipal Hospital Survey (Encuestas y Estudios, 1998).

Notes: Percentages may not add up to 100 due to rounding.

and public-works-related corruption as being most frequent. Within the health sector itself, doctors and nurses point to theft of medical supplies, misreferral of patients to the private sector, and payments for scheduling procedures as being most prominent. Finally most respondents believe that health-related corruption has decreased during the past five years. Patients are particularly optimistic about recent improvements. In more general terms, 65 percent of doctors, 72 percent of patients, and 80 percent of nurses believe that corruption in the health sector is less than or equal to levels in other social institutions.

Determinants of Informal Payments

The "informality" of informal payments is difficult to conceptualize, let alone measure. Since not all informal payments are unethical or illegal (some may supplement medical treatment initiated elsewhere; others may be regarded as ex post, service gratuities), this analysis is directed toward those forms that are illegal and explicitly proscribed by existing legislation and by administrative regulations of the Seguro Materno Infantil. Data was collected on informal payments relating to hospitalization, surgery, medication, materials and supplies, lab work, x-rays, and other service treatments covered by the Seguro. By restricting the analysis to this subset, the dependent variable will measure only illegal informal payments, and hence will not capture other forms of under-the-table payments that may skirt the lines between ethical norms and formal rules and regulations. We expect this measure to underestimate the extent of informal payments between patients and service providers.

The main finding is that approximately 40 percent of surveyed clients (112 of 281) reported making illegal payments under one of the Seguro's three subprograms. Because some two-thirds of respondents considered hospitals to be less or equally prone to corruption as other institutions in society, this result would suggest a high degree of tolerance of petty bribery. In other words, if 40 percent of respondents paid bribes and still thought hospitals were less corrupt than other social institutions, it must reflect very poorly on those other institutions.

Does citizen voice help prevent corruption? The analysis hypothesizes that voice should deter corruption by raising the probability that illegal payments are detected, thus increasing the expected cost of malfeasance. It is also hypothesized that hierarchical controls that detect and punish corruption deter public wrongdoing. In principle, hierarchical controls can be analyzed at many levels of aggregation (hospital controls, municipal controls, ministry auditing, comptroller auditing, administrative and civil justice courts, and so on). This study focuses exclusively on municipal-level hierarchical controls related to local hospital administration.

Three alternative specifications were run to test whether hierarchical or voice/exit factors could account for illegal informal payments (see Table 2.9). The first specification is an OLS regression that measures the impact of hierarchical and voice variables on the payment amount after controlling for individual and municipal-level characteristics. The second OLS regression controls for heteroskedasticity (using robust standard errors) and for aggregation bias (clustering individual observations into municipal clusters) from the use of multilevel data pooled in the same regression. The third specification is a tobit regression that controls for lower-bound censoring of illegal payments. We believe the tobit specification best tests the empirical relationship because a combination of voice and hierarchical con-

Table 2.9 Determinants of Illegal Informal Payments

	(1)		(2)		(3)	
	OLS	$P > |t|$	OLS adjusted	$P > |t|$	Tobit censored	$P > |t|$
Control variables						
Municipal poverty rate	−1.23	0.017	−1.23	0.003	−6.68	0.000
Client heard of Seguro	−0.17	0.523	−1.79	0.080	−0.37	0.537
Client waited more than 4 hours	27.20	0.000	27.20	0.004	59.54	0.000
Hierarchical controls						
Competitive hiring in municipality	−3.32	0.716	3.32	0.789	−54.42	0.021
Municipal personnel supervision	−15.37	0.223	−15.37	0.164	−14.41	0.668
Voice/Exit						
Voice: DILOS is active in annual planning process	−26.91	0.002	−26.91	0.004	−144.82	0.000
Exit: Competition from other service providers	−0.01	0.000	−0.00	0.000	−73.27	0.063
Constant	12.11		12.11		183.90	
Number of observations	281		281		281	
Clusters	0		24		11	
Pseudo R^2	0.134		0.159		0.045	

Source: Municipal Hospital Survey (Encuestas y Estudios, 1998).

Notes: The dependent variable is informal payments (in bolivares) reported by patients who received services under the Seguro Materno Infantil, including in-hospital payments for hospitalization, surgery, medication, materials and supplies, lab work, x-rays. Voluntary payments and out-of-hospital payments are excluded. The municipal poverty rate is measured by the basic needs index.

trols could potentially offer more-than-necessary anticorruption protection, and yet illegal payments would still not drop below 0.

The OLS specifications suggest three main results. First, the municipal poverty level and client waiting hours are significantly correlated with informal payments. That is, the higher the poverty rate, the lower the payments, and the longer the waiting hours, the higher the payments. Second, after controlling for individual and municipal characteristics, citizen-health-board activism, proxied by DILOS participation in municipal participatory planning, is significantly correlated to lower payments. Although both voice and exit variables are statistically significant, only the voice variable shows a coefficient that is not negligible. After controlling for an array of individual and municipal controls, the existence of an active citizen health board deters informal payments by Bs 26 (about US$4.33). The third result is that hierarchical control variables (a competitive hiring system and a personnel supervision system) are negatively correlated with informal payments but less significant than the voice/exit variables. Hierarchical controls appear to be less important than the voice/exit variables in deterring corruption.

The tobit model confirms the OLS regression results, but suggests the impact of voice and exit variables is larger once one controls for lower-bound censoring. After controlling for an array of individual and municipal characteristics, citizen board activism (DILOS) would account for Bs 144 less of informal payments (about US$24). The existence of a private health service provider also diminishes the amount of average informal payments by Bs 73 (US$12). Under the tobit model one hierarchical control variable, a competitive hiring system, acts as a deterrent to corruption, while the other, a personnel management system, remains statistically insignificant.

All specifications suggest that voice and exit variables are significantly and negatively related to informal payments, once hierarchical and other control variables are taken into account. As suggested by the recent literature on voice and exit, the voice option is most likely to be significant where service users enter into direct contact with service providers, thereby raising the probability of detection (Bossert, 1997). The significance of the exit option would also suggest the importance of competition in curtailing public-sector corruption (Ades and Di Tella, 1997; Ades and Di Tella, 1995). When public providers face competition from private providers and depend on user-cost recovery for recurrent financing, exit effectively raises the price of noncompliance. How effective is the voice option? While average informal payments are Bs 40 (US$6.67) per service user, a voice mechanism can account for Bs 27 (US$4.50) per user (about two-thirds of the average). The survey of patients under the Seguro Materno Infantil would suggest the voice option is a powerful deterrent to illegal informal payments.

Determinants of Input Overpricing

The analysis of supply prices provides a more direct yardstick of the degree of corrupt or particularistic behavior in the health sector. Prices were col-

Table 2.10 Variations in Medical Supply Prices Paid by Bolivian Hospitals (Bolivares, 1998)

	N	Min	Max	Mean	Variance
5% Dextrose solution	24	2.04	8.75	6.39	3.75
Normal saline solution	18	1.20	18.50	7.64	6.02
Absorbent cotton	16	0.80	28.60	15.64	65.24
Ethyl alcohol	13	1.30	8.00	5.39	3.11

Source: Municipal Hospital Survey (Encuestas y Estudios, 1998).

Note: The exchange rate in 1998 was approximately Bs 6 = US$1.

lected for four relatively homogeneous and widely available inputs: 5 percent dextrose solution, normal saline solution, absorbent cotton, and ethyl alcohol.[2] Input prices are nominally set at the Ministry of Health but show wide variations (see Table 2.10). While the official price of dextrose, for example, is set at Bs 5/liter, municipal receipts in 24 municipalities show a high-low price spread from Bs 2.04 to Bs 8.75. Part of this variation may be due to overpricing at the municipal level. In order to test this hypothesis, and analyze the determinants of price variations, alternative regressions were run on the ratio between actual prices paid by hospitals and the officially regulated supply prices. For the purposes of the econometric analysis, the differences in dextrose prices were used because there was more data on this item than on the others.

Two OLS regressions measure the effects of administrator characteristics and the presence or absence of hierarchical controls and citizen voice on supply prices (see Table 2.11). The variables that best explain variation in supply prices relate to the personal characteristics of the hospital administrator (tenure, education) and voice (DILOS).

When the administrator has held his or her job for a longer time, the ratio between actual and official prices tends to be lower. It could be that more-experienced administrators do a better job of negotiating prices or following policies. Alternatively, in a context of politicized and discretion-

---

[2] Prices were copied from official purchase receipts provided by municipal hospital administrators. Prices were later standardized to comparable units of analysis.

ary administration, longer job tenure may be an indicator of job security and institutionalized hiring practices that discourage corruption.

The findings for education, however, are more problematic. Controlling for other factors, the model finds that education is positively correlated to overpricing. The positive sign would suggest that well-educated administrators are more likely to engage in fraud, perhaps being more effective at hiding abuses. If this were really true, it suggests that, given the current incentive structure, policies designed to hire more-qualified administrators would promote rather than deter public-sector corruption.

Are agency problems a driving factor behind this result? While it was expected that personnel supervision and access to local distribution centers would be negatively and significantly correlated to input overpricing, the findings for these hierarchical control variables were inconclusive. Personnel supervision proved to be only weakly correlated to overpricing, and the presence of a local input distribution center was not significant at all. The only other significant and negatively correlated variable is voice (DILOS). The presence of an activist citizen health board is, in fact, the most important deterrent of input overpricing. Citizen voice accounted for approximately 40 percent of the variation between actual and official prices. Other control variables were not significant in explaining input price variations.

What role do voice mechanisms play in deterring hidden fraud? Controlling for administrator characteristics and hierarchical control variables, our estimates suggest voice mechanisms are remarkably effective. Citizen activism accounts for approximately 40 percent of the variation between official and purchased prices. Given the low levels of significance of hierarchical control variables, perhaps the more relevant question is what role do administrative controls play in deterring and punishing corrupt actions? The analysis suggests a qualified answer. While hierarchical control variables are not significantly correlated to corruption deterrence, administrator job tenure is found to be significantly and negatively correlated to overpricing. To the extent that tenure length is construed as a proxy of institutional stability, factors that promote stable employment can be regarded as additional deterrents to corrupt practice. The low R^2 on both specifications also suggests that much remains unexplained in this model, including political and administrative deterrents of corruption working beyond the local level (prefectural or line-ministry controls).

Table 2.11 Determinants of Supply Prices

	(1)	$P > |t|$	(2)	$P > |t|$
Control variables				
Administrator tenure in job (years)	−0.014	0.007	−0.015	0.010
Administrator years of schooling	0.016	0.033	0.016	0.039
Municipal poverty rate	−0.006	0.242	−0.005	0.416
Hierarchical variables				
Personnel supervision system	−0.345	0.202	−0.372	0.103
Municipal distribution center			0.092	0.674
Voice/Exit variables				
DILOS is active in annual planning process	−0.426	0.040	−0.404	0.064
Oversight Committee is active in annual planning process			0.203	0.345
Constant	2.057		1.972	
Number of observations	24		24	
Adjusted R^2	0.303		0.270	

Source: Municipal Hospital Survey (Encuestas y Estudios, 1998).

Notes: The dependent variable is the ratio of the price paid by hospitals to the official price for 5% dextrose solution, with the former standardized by purchase volume and the latter provided by the Ministry of Health. The municipal poverty rate is measured by the basic needs index.

Hard and Soft Data Comparisons

Much of the literature on transparency and accountability has analyzed data derived from public opinion surveys and polls. Few studies have collected empirical data on the scope and determinants of corruption; fewer have compared both types of data for the same sample. This subsection compares "hard" and "soft" indices of municipal corruption. Municipalities with high levels of corruption indicated by informal payments and input overpricing are compared to municipalities where corruption was perceived to be high in surveys of service users.

The correlation between informal payments and perceived corruption is positive and significant (0.551). In general terms, the perception that

Figure 2.1 Correlation between Informal Payments and Perceptions of Corruption

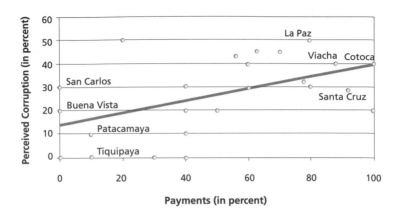

Notes: "Perceived corruption" refers to the share of service users who described hospital corruption to be greater than or equal to corruption elsewhere in the public or private sector; "payments" refers to the share of service users who reported making illegal informal payments.

hospitals are more (or equally) corrupt than other public- or private-sector institutions is positively correlated with a higher incidence of informal payments. The strongest incidences of actual and perceived corruption occur in the capital cities and relatively large municipalities; the weakest occur in small rural municipalities (Figure 2.1). How can this pattern be explained? One possibility is that perceptions and acts of corruption are highly sensitive to the scale of health service delivery. Although the hospitals in our sample are roughly of the same size, evidence suggests that larger hospitals do in fact show a higher incidence of both actual and perceived corruption. A second possibility is that the market for informal payments — contrasted for example, with the market for petty theft or input overpricing — is more sensitive to the "large hospital" effect. This may account for substantial differences between informal payments in one-doctor hospitals (in which they are largely absent) and multilevel hierarchical organizations (in which they are more significant). Agency problems, enhanced by size, might be the main culprit.

A weaker, but also positive correlation (0.214) was found between input overpricing and perceived corruption. The perception that hospitals are

Figure 2.2 Correlation between Input Overpricing and Perceptions of Corruption

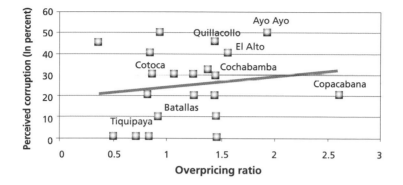

Notes: "Perceived corruption" refers to the share of service users who described hospital corruption to be greater than or equal to corruption elsewhere in the public or private sector; "overpricing ratio" refers to the ratio of actually paid to officially set prices for 5% dextrose solution (adjusted for volume).

at least as corrupt as other public- or private-sector institutions is positively correlated to the degree of price variations in dextrose and normal-saline solutions. The distribution of actual and perceived corruption is not as dependent on hospital size as with informal payments. Findings of perceived and actual corruption are scattered for large and small hospitals alike (Figure 2.2). What accounts for this result? As discussed in the previous section, the hidden nature of the abuse suggests that the existence of personnel management, public procurement, and auditing capabilities are more important than hospital size as deterrents to overpricing. The most relevant contrast, in this case, is between highly discretionary and often politicized municipal administrations and those that are not.

What can be learned from these hard and soft data comparisons? The positive correlations suggest that perceptions of corruption generally mirror the available hard evidence on public-sector corruption. It should be noted, however, that the correlation for services in which users are directly involved is higher than when discretionary actions go unobserved. As suggested earlier, the use of citizen voice is likely to be correlated with public perceptions of wrongdoing. The greater the perception of corruption, the more likely it is that citizens will make use of voice mechanisms and monitor public-service delivery. In more general terms, the hard and soft data comparisons are reassuring. Analyses based on public opinion polls and surveys are, on this account, consistent with the available evidence on corrupt practice: the greater the corruption, the greater the perception of corruption.

Conclusions

This chapter has focused on the scope and determinants of corruption in the public health sector in Bolivia. It defines corruption broadly to mean the use or appropriation of public resources for private gain. The politics of transparency, accountability, and corruption have attracted a great deal of notoriety, but little empirical work has focused on the institutional mechanisms that restrict or encourage corrupt public practices. This analysis of municipal hospitals in Bolivia uses a simple model to account for the potential effects of hierarchical controls (mostly administrative) and voice mechanisms (mostly market based) on hospital-level corruption.

How significant is health sector corruption in Bolivia, and what factors account for corrupt public practice? The survey of clients, doctors, and nurses in 30 municipal hospitals found that perceptions of health sector corruption fare well when compared to other public- and private-sector institutions. Most respondents believe public hospitals are among the least corrupt institutions, together with public schools and the Catholic Church. When asked to assess the frequency of corrupt acts in the public sector, most respondents identify corruption related to red tape and public works as being most frequent. Within the health sector itself, doctors and nurses point to theft of medical supplies, misreferral of patients, and payments for scheduling procedures as being most prominent. Finally, most respondents believe corruption in the health sector has decreased in the past five years. Doctors are most critical of health sector corruption, while patients are least critical. This descriptive assessment set the stage for an analysis of the determinants of corruption within the public health sector.

First, the scope and determinants of informal payments to service providers were examined. Despite the relatively optimistic picture suggested by public perceptions, this study found that approximately 40 percent of clients made illegal informal payments to service providers and administrators under the Seguro Materno Infantil. Controlling for municipal poverty levels and patient waiting hours, four variables were significant in explaining payment variations under alternative specifications: the degree of activism of the local citizen health board (–), the existence of alternative private-sector health providers (–), administrative supervision of health staff (–), and competitive hiring practices (–). Voice and exit mechanisms are clearly important deterrents of illegal informal payments at the local level. The literature on voice has stressed the effect that competition in service delivery can have over institutional performance (Paul, 1994; Picciotto, 1997). This chapter suggests that voice is best assessed after controlling for more-conventional hierarchical controls over public accountability. Competition between public and private service providers is likely to be most effective in increasing the price of noncompliance when public providers are dependent on user-cost recovery for service financing.

Second, the scope and determinants of input overpricing for homogeneous and widely available medical supplies (5 percent dextrose solution, normal saline solution, absorbent cotton, and ethyl alcohol) were analyzed. Findings showed that, even for a small survey of prices in 24 municipalities, standardized prices for medical supplies vary significantly. Controlling for municipal poverty levels, analysis of a single input (5 percent dextrose) found three significant determinants of price variation: administrator education (+), length of job tenure (–), and health board activism (–). To a lesser extent, the existence of a personnel supervision system also deters overpricing (–). Voice played a key role in deterring overpricing, and accounted for a 40 percent differential between official and purchased prices. The evidence also tentatively suggests that administrative regimes that promote competitive and supervised hiring and management practices are more likely to reduce overpricing than regimes relying on political patronage and arbitrary practices.

Third, hard and soft measures of corruption at the municipal level were compared. Findings showed that public perceptions of corruption were positively correlated to higher incidences of informal payments and input overpricing. The greater the corruption was, the greater was the perception of corruption. High actual and perceived levels of corruption tended to concentrate in larger municipalities. Smaller, particularly rural, municipalities showed low levels of both indices. The correlation was also higher for services in which users are directly involved than for discretionary actions that go unobserved. As suggested earlier, the use of citizen voice is likely to be correlated with public perceptions of wrongdoing. The greater the perception of corruption, the more likely it is that citizens will make use of voice mechanisms and monitor public-service delivery.

What are the implications of these findings for transparency, accountability, and corruption in the public health sector? From an analytical perspective, the measurement of corrupt public practice should be institution-sensitive to account for the particularities of different types of corrupt behavior. In the Bolivian case, the decentralized and participatory characteristics of the health delivery system were characterized through a model that controls for hierarchical constraints and voice and exit variables. When perceptions from different groups and for different types of practices were compared, the very definition of corruption came into question. It is likely, although untested through available data, that the public's threshold for petty corruption is relatively high in Bolivia. While nearly 40 percent of surveyed patients acknowledged having made an (illegal) informal payment of one kind or another, over two-thirds of patients, nurses, and doctors rate health sector corruption as being equally or less corrupt than other public- and private-sector institutions. Only 19 percent of patients, 18 percent of doctors, and 27 percent of nurses considered hospital corruption to be widespread (with corrupt acts being carried out "a lot" or "all" of the time).

From a public policy perspective, this chapter has focused on the particular question of citizen voice and public accountability. When does voice matter as a deterrent to corruption in the public sector? We find that voice matters both for exposing bribery (when it directly involves citizen contact) and for deterring input overpricing (characterized by hidden fraud within the health bureaucracy). In both cases, voice involved citizen health board activism, as proxied by the board's role in annual participatory planning, budgeting, and oversight. In the case of bribery, the "exit" option, as proxied by the existence of private health service providers, was also significantly correlated to corruption deterrence.

How well do hierarchical controls, which are expected to deter (ex ante) and punish (ex post) corrupt behavior, actually work? Unlike voice, no consistent evidence was found to suggest that hierarchical controls deter corruption. In the case of bribery only one hierarchical variable was significant (competitive hiring practices, at 5 percent); in the case of overpricing, practically none (personnel supervision, at 10 percent). The evidence on hierarchical controls is inconclusive, and this doubt is compounded by the observation that both models explain only a small proportion of variation in our key dependent variables. The low fit may also mean that omitted political and administrative factors (at the prefectural or national level) account for the overall impact of hierarchical controls in corruption deterrence.

Citizen involvement in public services has many effects above and beyond controlling corruption, such as building support for democratic principles, promoting a sense of ownership with regard to public policy, creating a more inclusive society, and extending empowerment. But this study has also shown that in very practical terms strengthening citizen voice, establishing transparency, and increasing accountability can reduce fraud and abuse. In this sense, greater citizen involvement is at the core of efforts to make governance more effective. Voice is not merely an expression of basic liberties; it is also an institutional tool for deterring corruption in the provision of social services.

CHAPTER 3

Wages, Capture and Penalties in Venezuela's Public Hospitals

María Helena Jaén and Daniel Paravisini

Three types of corruption were reported to be common in Venezuela's public hospitals: graft in purchases of medical supplies; theft or pilferage of supplies and medicines; and absenteeism among doctors and nurses. Looking at these illegal activities through a traditional model of criminal behavior and agency theory, it was possible to evaluate the impact of institutional design on the extent of corruption. In particular, the probability of detection and sanction appeared to play a large role in explaining theft and absenteeism. The probabilities of detection and sanction are, in turn, associated with the existence of administrative controls and with independent management of human resources by the hospital director, respectively. By contrast, pay levels appeared to have no impact on theft and, if anything, were associated with higher prices paid for supply purchases. Because the simple agency model was unable to explain differences in overpayment, it may be necessary to develop a more sophisticated model of illegal behavior that would incorporate the possibility of collusion between administrators and their staff.

Introduction

In Venezuela a widespread perception exists that corruption is seriously affecting the quality of health services provided by public hospitals. Many senior government health officials and hospital directors express alarm at the level of illegal activities and are concerned about the conditions that allow it to continue. This chapter addresses these concerns by analyzing the relationship between the incentive structure associated with the institutional design of public hospitals and corruption defined as *illegal activities that reduce the economic efficiency of hospitals.*[1] In particular it asks whether the probabilities of detection and punishment, along with the severity of imposed penalties, affect the corruption level in public hospitals, thereby compromising their ability to provide effective services. A better understanding of these institutional levers will have clear implications for policy formulation and for establishing and implementing procedures to improve performance.

Illegal activities in the public sector are, of course, not restricted to public hospitals. In fact corruption is denounced daily in many spheres of Venezuelan life, and public perception of widespread abuse contributed to defeat of the country's traditional parties in recent elections. Nevertheless illegal activities in public hospitals, whose services can make the difference between life and death, are of particular concern.

Within Venezuela's public hospitals, graft in medical supply purchases, theft of supplies and medicines, and absenteeism among doctors and nurses are considered the most common and problematic illegal practices. This chapter will demonstrate that clear evidence exists of a relationship between the institutional mechanisms designed to detect, reveal, and punish illegal activity and the level of corruption, and will identify which managerial instruments are deficient or lacking.

Venezuela's Health System and the Role of Public Hospitals

The Venezuelan health system, which involves both the public and private sectors, is very complex organizationally and functionally. The public component includes several agencies that provide finances, insurance, and services. These include the Ministry of Health and Social Development, or Ministerio de Salud y Desarrollo Social (MSDS); the Venezuelan Institute of Social Security, or Instituto Venezolano de los Seguros Sociales (IVSS); the Welfare and Social Assistance Institute of the Education Ministry, or Instituto de Previsión y Asistencia Social del Ministerio de Educación (IPASME); the Armed Forces Institute of Social Welfare, or Instituto de Previsión Social de las Fuerzas Armadas (IPSFA); as well as state and local governments.

---

[1] This definition is adapted from Mauro (1997) who defines corrupt practices in the public sector as "illegal activities that reduce the economic efficiency of government."

A wide range of nongovernmental actors, which can be roughly sub-divided into two groups, complements the public structure. Commercial insurance and private health care providers cover the higher social strata, while nongovernmental organizations (NGOs), nonprofit cooperatives, and charitable foundations serve those who lack any other coverage or who have access to public services but choose not to use them.

As a result of the decentralization that began at the end of the 1980s,[2] an intergovernmental health system was set up that divided responsibilities among the national, state, and local levels (González, 1997a and 1997b). In the process, states have assumed powers that were previously reserved exclusively for the central government. By law MSDS and the state governments that have assumed jurisdiction over health care must provide services for people who lack public or private health insurance, estimated at between 30 and 40 percent of the population. The IVSS covers approximately 37 percent of the population, providing a form of public insurance for workers in the formal economy and their families. The rest of the population should be covered by other forms of public insurance such as IPASME and IPSFA, but many also purchase their own insurance or services from the private sector, or seek care from nonprofit providers. Although this disparate network of health care establishments theoretically covers all levels of treatment, centers equipped to handle more-complex cases also provide basic services. This generates problems of accessibility and equity since outpatient facilities do not have adequate capacity, and people seeking care view hospitals as their best option for getting treatment.

In 1996, a report by the MSDS (1997 and 1998) stated that the occupancy rate was 63.6 percent, with an average in-patient stay of 5.3 days and a turnover rate of 44.3 patients per bed. In 1997, occupancy fell, reaching 60.7 percent, with an average stay of 5 days and a nearly unchanged turn-

---

[2] Service transfers from MSDS began in 1989 with enactment of the Organic Law of Decentralization and Transfer of Powers of the Public Authorities, and the direct election of state governors. In the same year, transfer negotiations began with some states, with five states signing agreements at the end of 1993. On June 22, 1998, the Ministry signed over 9 hospitals and 56 outpatient centers to the government of the Federal District. By October 1998, another 16 decentralization agreements had been established with the states of Falcón, Anzoátegui, Carabobo, Aragua, Bolívar, Zulia, Mérida, Trujillo, Táchira, Sucre, Lara, Monagas, Miranda, Nueva Esparta, Apure, and Yaracuy. Joint management agreements have been signed with the states of Barinas, Cojedes, Guárico, and Portuguesa. The transfer requested by Delta Amacuro was, at the time of writing, still being processed.

over rate of 44.7. Data reported by the IVSS (1998) showed that occupancy rates for their hospitals were between 70 percent and 80 percent in Level-I hospitals, and 75 percent and 85 percent in hospitals of Levels II, III, and IV.[3] The average stay varied from three to four days for the gynecology-obstetrics service, and 10 to 14 days for the other services (pediatrics, medicine, and surgery). Both institutions employed, on average, about five health professionals per bed, which is higher than the international standard of two to four professionals. These overall figures are similar to those found by a World Bank (1992) study with data from 1987 and 1988. However, the World Bank study also demonstrated a much greater difference between hospitals, finding that occupancy in general hospitals, Levels I and II, was less than 30 percent. On the other hand, the number of emergency visits to hospitals and outpatient departments was much higher than preventive visits, which do not reach 60 percent of the potential target population. In surgical operations, emergencies predominated over planned operations (Jaén et al., 1997).

This is consistent with evidence of distortions in the operation of the health service network, and thus in the pattern of treatment, since most of the population receives treatment at the hospital level, irrespective of the seriousness or complexity of the health problem.

Three problems emerge as likely causes for poor hospital performance: financing, institutional design, and the system of health staff accountability. This chapter examines the hypothesis that institutional variables, such as the systems of incentives and accountability, are the primary factors. Before testing that hypothesis, however, one must first determine if the most obvi-

---

[3] According to current legal provisions, Level I hospitals provide basic primary and secondary medical, surgical, gynecological-obstetric, and pediatric services. They have 20 to 60 beds and serve localities of less than 20,000 inhabitants, with a catchment-area of up to 60,000. In addition to these services, Level II hospitals provide some tertiary care, as well as cardiological, psychiatric, dermatologic, venereal disease, pneumonology, orthopedic, ophthalmologic, and ear-nose-and-throat services. They have 60 to 150 beds and serve localities of over 20,000 inhabitants, with a catchment-area of up to 100,000. Level III hospitals provide comprehensive medical services at all three clinical levels. They have 150 to 300 beds and serve localities with over 60,000 inhabitants, and a catchment-area of up to 400,000. Finally, Level IV hospitals have more than 300 beds and also provide comprehensive medical services at all levels. They cover populations of over 100,000, and have catchment-areas that include over 1 million inhabitants. For a complete description of the classification of hospitals, see the Republic of Venezuela (1983).

ous possibility — a reduction in hospital resource allocations — is the key to deteriorating public services.

Although government health expenditures have been declining rapidly in recent years, total spending for the sector is still higher than in other Latin American countries.[4] And Venezuela is among the leaders in the percentage of health system resources allocated to hospitals (Barnum and Kutzin, 1993). An analysis of trends shows that between 1990 and 1997 the share of the national budget spent on health declined from 13.3 percent to 9.3 percent. Estimates for 1996 reveal that total health sector spending accounted for approximately 6.6 percent of GDP, with public and private expenditures accounting for 1.9 percent and 4.7 percent, respectively. In the 1980–1997 period, public spending on health averaged approximately 2 percent of GDP, but annual spending per capita fell from US$109 to US$84.40 (Salvato, 1998). Meanwhile private expenditures by household for medical care and hospitalization moved in the opposite direction, rising substantially between 1984 and 1995.[5]

Most of the MSDS budget involves personnel costs. In the 1989–1995 period, over 72 percent of funds were for payrolls, a figure that rose to 79.3 percent in 1995. Workers and administrative staff (nonmedical personnel) accounted for 52 percent of payroll expenses (Jaén et al, 1997; Salvato, 1998). Thirty percent of the total resources of MSDS were used for central administration, nonmedical systems, and public health programs. Of the rest, 71 percent was allocated to the hospital network, 17 percent to primary care, and the remaining 12 percent to other management expenditures (Consorcio Hospitalario de Catalunya, 1997). According to the World Bank (1992), the estimated percentage of MSDS spending on hospitals between 1980 and 1990 moved from 80 percent in the first year to a maximum of 86 percent in 1983 and 1984, before falling to 71 percent in the last year of the series. The IVSS

---

[4] In 1990, according to the Pan-American Health Organization, Venezuela spent US$220 per person on health. In the same year, average per capita health spending was US$105 in Latin America and US$1,860 in developed countries. These estimates confirm that total and per capita health spending in Venezuela are higher than in other Andean countries, such as Colombia withUS$82.20 per capita, Ecuador with US$78.60, Peru with US$41.30, and Bolivia with US$39.00 (PAHO, 1994).

[5] The distribution of public and private health spending does not reflect real coverage. Public spending, with all its limitations, covers a large proportion of the population, while 80 percent of private coverage is concentrated in the highest-income quartiles (Salvato, 1998).

(1998) reports a similar trend, with 74 percent of its budget earmarked for hospitals in 1990.

If Venezuela spends more on health than other Latin American countries and most of that flow goes to hospitals, then resource availability does not appear to be at the root of deteriorating services. Does the institutional design of Venezuelan public hospitals, then, lead to inefficient management and use of available financial resources, and hamper the ability of hospital directors to improve performance? The World Bank study (1992) indicates that public hospitals either have no management control systems or very limited ones. Moreover these hospitals have very restricted budgetary independence, precarious or nonexistent cost-accounting systems, and a widespread practice of unregulated direct and indirect patient billing. Discretion over hiring is limited since the MSDS, IVSS, and state governments control almost all decisions at the central level. Consequently hiring is uncommon by MSDS hospitals, and accounts for only 5 percent of IVSS hospital budgets. Furthermore hospitals have little control over purchase of supplies, medicines, and medical equipment since these, too, are mostly centralized in the capital. There is an incipient initiative to transform hospitals into autonomous facilities, and some states have used their new powers from the decentralization process to actively promote this novel form of management. As a result, new institutional designs and incentive structures are being created that could affect corrupt practices in hospitals.

One factor that significantly affects internal accountability in hospitals is the limited control that public hospitals have over their human resources, resulting in excessive employment.[6] Unions and professional organizations have accumulated enough power to undermine the capacity and independence of public officials to manage their human resources. Labor regulations are formulated at the highest level of government, with little or no input from public hospital administrations. Labor negotiations in the health sector have become a perverse and almost ritualized exercise between

---

[6] The ratio of doctors to inhabitants grew steadily between 1970 and 1995 from 8.6 to 20.4 per 10,000, double the ratio of 10 per 10,000 recommended by WHO. The increase in professional nurses was smaller, rising from 4 per 10,000 inhabitants in 1970 to 8.4 per 10,000 inhabitants in 1995. Seventeen of the 27 Latin American countries have a ratio of 10 or fewer doctors per 10,000. Venezuela is among those with an excessive number of doctors, along with Uruguay and Argentina where there were 36.8 and 26.8 doctors per 10,000 in habitants, respectively (PAHO, 1992).

unequal forces. After a round of threats and job actions, the government and unions finally agree to commit economic resources that the government does not possess, thus postponing the underlying issues until the new agreement inevitably collapses.

The collective bargaining system for labor in the sector is grounded in the traditional value of standardized working conditions for all workers at the same hierarchical level, which undermines any attempt to introduce wage innovations, such as linking pay to productivity. Finally, most public hospitals have no power over crucial areas of personnel administration such as selection, hiring, and dismissal of professionals and workers. These functions are reserved for higher administrative levels where unions and professional organizations are able to exert great pressure. Consequently most hospitals have limited capacity to punish irregular activities. This, in turn, creates a climate of blatant impunity, favoring every kind of corrupt practice.[7]

This financial, institutional, and administrative framework for human resources has fostered a widespread view that hospital performance is hampered by improper management practices. To identify areas of mismanagement, key informants were consulted, including seven officials who hold or once held high-level positions in the health system (an ex-minister, a health network director, health directors in the states, among others), nine hospital directors, and three medical equipment suppliers.

These informants identified three areas of corruption that are of great concern to the functioning of the hospitals: overpayment (kickbacks) on purchases of medical supplies and medicines; theft of supplies and medicines; and absenteeism.

Before studying these in greater detail, it is useful to consider the theory underpinning how these practices are associated with low pay and poor professional training; institutional weaknesses (failures in information, supervision, control, registration, and security systems, and the lack of performance measurement systems); existence of multiple decision-makers (multiple principals) and interference by professional organizations and unions in health personnel management; impunity (a perception of low probability for de-

---

[7] The authors would like to acknowledge José Ramón Padilla, professor at the Instituto de Estudios Superiores de Administración in Caracas, who provided this section on health personnel accountability.

tection and punishment); social acquiescence to the different forms of corruption; and lack of institutional commitment and loss of values by health personnel.

Theoretical Determinants of Corruption

As mentioned in the introduction, this chapter defines corruption as *illegal activities that reduce hospital efficiency*. Other definitions, such as "the abuse of public power for private benefit" used by Tanzi (1998) or "the sale of State property by public officials to obtain private benefit" used by Shleifer and Vishny (1993) add private benefit as the motivating factor. However, in the case of hospitals, the impact of such irregularities on the provision of health services is of much greater importance than whether or not the activities lead to personal enrichment. Hence, this chapter will place greater emphasis on the effects of corruption on hospital performance. Using the premises of the economic theories of the agent-principal relationship and of crime (Becker, 1968; Becker and Stigler, 1974), this chapter will analyze how institutional design and incentives can discourage or encourage corrupt practices and thereby hinder an efficient allocation and utilization of resources.

Using these premises, corruption can be interpreted as a diversion of agents' actions from the interests of the "principal" (Bardhan, 1997). More complexly, it can be visualized as a chain of relations between agents who commit corrupt acts and principals who detect and punish those acts. Marjit and Shi (1998) go even further, introducing the possibility that the principals are also corrupt, and therefore able to negotiate and collude with agents in committing illegal acts.

This study posits a chain of principal-agent relationships that begins with citizens and ends with the hospital personnel who deliver health services. It starts from the premise that elected government officials are agents of the citizenry and represent the people's interests through the formulation and implementation of public policies. In turn, public hospitals are administered by directors who are agents responding to the orders of those elected officials. Finally the provision of hospital services is the responsibility of doctors, nurses, and other health professionals, and administrative staff who work under the hospital director. The relationships between all the principals and agents in this chain are determined by "contracts" represented by formal and informal rules and procedures. The final behavior of agents will be influenced by this set of relationships, rules, and procedures, which together form the "institutional design."

Institutional design shapes agent conduct through incentives built into the principal-agent relationship. The incentives implicit in the institutional design are intended to align the interests of the agents with those of the principal. That is, a good incentive system will reward agents most when they achieve the objectives set out by the principal.

When the institutional design does not generate a set of rules or incentives that aligns the interests of the principals and the agents in this way, the latter, acting rationally for their own benefit, will not necessarily exert the level of effort required by their commitment to the principal. This is because the principal can only measure the agent's effort indirectly through observation of the results, which are noisy measures of actual effort (Macho Stadler and Pérez Castrillo, 1994; Rasmusen, 1996).

From this point of view, illegal activities in hospitals will be most common where hospital staff pursue their own interests in weighing the benefits of proper or improper behavior. If they behave properly, they can expect to receive their wages. If they act improperly, they can expect to benefit from the illegal activity, but also face some probability of being detected and punished (perhaps even losing their jobs). The staff's level of effort will be affected, then, by the difference between potential gain from corrupt actions and the amount of their wages minus what they would earn from alternative forms of employment. That is, behavior will be influenced by the character of the employment contract, which sometimes links pay to effort, productivity, or outputs. It will also be affected by the agent's attitude toward risk.

This framework leads to several hypotheses regarding how institutional design and incentives can affect the level of corruption by influencing expected benefits. In particular the expected benefits from, and consequently the level of, corruption will be higher whenever the (1) expected income from corruption is higher, (2) probability of being detected and punished is lower, or (3) penalties are lower.

A hospital's institutional design influences the level of corruption since it affects the expected benefit from illegal activities. It does so by altering the individual's expected income, the probability of detection, the probability that punishment will follow detection, and the expected magnitude of any applicable punishment.

Expected income is modified by potential income and the opportunities for corruption, which rise with the volume and value of the purchases or transactions involving the agent, and with increases in the agent's discretionary authority.

The *probability of detection* is affected by the degree of control and supervision that the principal can exercise over the agents in the use of financial resources, medical supplies, and work time. Principals exercise control and supervision through a variety of mechanisms, depending on the type of conduct they wish to modify. These include setting up systems to supervise work attendance and the use of materials; controls on purchase prices; systems for measuring the performance achieved with a given level of physical and human inputs; and the inclusion of users — citizens — to monitor, pressure, or even manage the facility.

The probability of detection is also associated with elements that are not directly controlled by the principals; for example, the likelihood of being caught increases when peer control is strong. Principals can stimulate positive peer pressure through pay schemes based on group performance, but the outcome also depends on the degree to which the individuals in the group consider corruption acceptable.

The *probability of punishment* depends on the principals' effective capacity to apply penalties once irregular conduct has been detected. This capacity weakens when the hospital director has no direct control over policies and decisions on pay, hiring, and dismissal of hospital staff. Hospital directors will lack such discretion when unions and professional organizations are given the power to hire personnel or to veto dismissals. It also occurs when hierarchical levels above the hospital director make contract decisions regarding pay, thereby preventing the directors from establishing effective sanctions.[8]

In general when agents in the organization respond to the mandates of multiple decision-makers, it will be more difficult for any one principal to control the conduct of agents. The existence of multiple mandates diffuses agents' responsibilities, weakening efforts to measure the agent's performance and prevents effective sanctions for undesirable conduct.

---

[8] The probability of applying sanctions also depends on the responsiveness and transparency of the authorities, especially the judiciary. Since these factors are the same for all hospitals, they cannot explain the differences in levels of inter- and intrahospital corruption.

The *size of the penalty* varies according to the type of offense. Depending on the seriousness and type of misconduct, sanctions can range from verbal warnings in the least serious to dismissal or criminal charges in the most serious cases. When punishment involves dismissal, the value of the penalty is the difference between existing pay for the job in the hospital and the amount the individual can expect from alternate employment. The higher this premium, the higher is the cost of dismissal.

Moving up the ladder of agency-principal relationships, the next step describes how the hospital director is the agent of higher government officials. This relationship is affected by the hospital's external institutional design, in other words, its governing body.

The level of corruption among hospital administrators (directors, supervisors, and managers) will also be influenced by the factors discussed previously: expected income, amount of penalty, probability of detection, and probability of punishment. Expected income depends in similar fashion on the potential income and benefits from corruption. The incentives to commit illegal activities will also be higher when the administrator or director oversees larger purchases or resources, and when discretionary authority is greater (*ceteris paribus*).

For hospital administration, the probabilities of detection and punishment are associated with the information available to higher officials about the actions of the hospital management and on their capacity to discipline improper conduct. The absence of controls on resource allocation, the multiplicity of decision makers with divergent mandates, and the size of the bureaucracy (number of agency relationships) existing between the primary principals (citizens) and the hospital management all reduce the likelihood of being able to assign responsibility and thus increase the agent's opportunities for corruption.

These factors do not imply that more independent hospital management always generates more corruption. When independence is accompanied by improved systems of control and accountability by the principal (i.e., elected officials or citizens), management becomes more flexible and can respond to incentives for applying resources in ways that further the interests of the principal. However granting greater discretionary authority to agents without modifying governance, oversight, and accountability can indeed increase deviations in the agent's conduct (i.e., corruption).

Characteristics of Sample Venezuelan Hospitals

The model of corruption will be applied empirically to a sample of 22 Venezuelan hospitals. The data used in the study were obtained from secondary sources of information, hospital records, interviews with key informants, and a survey of medical personnel at the hospitals. The sample hospitals are located in three states of central Venezuela, which rank among the top four states nationwide in terms of socioeconomic development and among the first six in terms of inhabitants (totaling about 6 million people or 25 percent of the national population in 1997). They are located in 10 urban areas with populations of between 20,000 and 4,000,000 inhabitants.

The hospitals were chosen to illustrate the range of institutional arrangements, levels of complexity, and legal forms present in Venezuela. Of the 22 hospitals, 20 are public hospitals operated by the MSDS (3), IVSS (3), the Defense Ministry (1), state governments with decentralization agreements (10), and state governments without decentralization agreements (3), with the remaining 2 hospitals operated as independent private facilities. The sample includes the spectrum of organizational complexity in general hospitals (Levels I, II, III, and IV), [9] but not specialty hospitals (e.g., psychiatric or obstetric). The hospitals have five different forms of legal status: some are privately held firms, while others are public foundations, government agencies, incorporated autonomous agencies, and autonomous but unincorporated facilities. The selection of hospitals also depended on the willingness of the health and hospital directors to participate in the study. A full description of sample hospital characteristics can be found in Jaén and Paravisini (1999).

Although the sample represents nearly the entire range of hospitals in terms of type of governing agency, level of complexity, and legal form, the research results should only be extrapolated with great caution. The sample can be interpreted as representative of the three particular states in which the research took place, but not construed to be representative of the country as a whole. [10] Nevertheless it does account for a substantial number of

---

[9] For a classification of establishments see footnote 3.

[10] The public-sector network of hospitals includes 239 establishments, while the private sector consists of 344 hospitals. The public sector finances some 35,000 hospital beds, while the private sector has almost 21,000.

hospitals within the states that were studied, accounting for 8.4 percent of the nation's public hospitals and 15.2 percent of the country's hospital beds.

Determinants of Overpayment

Informants indicated corrupt overpayment for supplies and medicines was extensive. Yet it is difficult to directly measure the degree of overpayment by a particular hospital or purchaser. Assuming that the differences in purchase prices paid by different hospitals for the same product were related to graft, we gathered information on monthly purchases of selected products for each hospital in the first half of 1998, with a total of 249 observations.[11] Empirical analysis was then used to control for alternative explanations of price differentials, such as variations in credit terms, bulk discounts, the efficiency of administrative procedures in the purchasing department, transportation costs (which depend on the distance between the hospital and distribution centers), or the ability of suppliers to exercise monopoly power.

Variation in purchasing procedures is especially important. Twelve of the 20 public hospitals have a procurement committee with between 2 and 9 members. All 22 hospitals use price comparison when possible. Eleven apply Venezuela's Procurement Law (Ley de Licitaciones). Six do not apply the Procurement Law, either because they are private hospitals or because they purchase amounts below the legal threshold; while five simply do not enforce the Law. Eight hospitals rely on reports of historical purchase prices, and five have some form of community participation in the hospital. Three hospitals report having had no audit the previous year, while the rest reported being audited from one to four times.

To select which products to track, the study used criteria proposed by Di Tella (1997): homogeneity and comparability. In other words, products were selected that did not have technical specification variations for medical, supplier, or brand requirements. Four products were chosen: normal saline solution at 0.9 percent in 500 ml bags, absorbent cotton in 500 gm rolls, 5 percent dextrose solution in 500 cc bags, and penicillin in 1 UI vials.

---

[11] In some cases, purchase frequency is less than one per month. In others the selected products were not purchased directly. As a result the number of observations per hospital varies between 1 and 24, with an average of 12.

The first step in establishing the relationship between price variation and overpayment is to observe the behavior of prices and purchase quantities between hospitals. Real purchase prices vary greatly for each product. The price variations are largest between hospitals, although there are also some price variations across time within particular hospitals for the same product (Table 3.1). The variations in purchase quantities are also important, particularly between hospitals, which may reflect the different sizes (number of beds) and complexities (type of services) of the hospitals in the sample.

Variations in purchase quantities are clearly quite large, and could be an important part of the explanation for both inter- and intrahospital price differences. Quantity can affect price when large purchases receive volume discounts, or when being a large purchaser is associated with being a hospital that has some significant market power. Under both interpretations, larger quantities for each purchase and overall purchase quantities of each product would be associated with lower prices.

To test this relationship, a price index weighted by quantities for each product was constructed, using all available data, to make the price data comparable for all products. The index was constructed by dividing the real price

Table 3.1 Range of Prices Paid and Quantities Purchased

	Total	Between hospitals	Within hospitals
Coefficient of variation of real prices paid			
Normal saline solution	30.8	27.7	11.6
Absorbent cotton	23.2	23.9	11.8
5% Dextrose solution	31.6	30.6	9.4
Penicillin	29.1	31.7	9.5
Coefficient of variation of quantities purchased			
Normal saline solution	147.5	147.6	40.3
Absorbent cotton	145.6	121.3	39.8
5% Dextrose solution	117.2	100.1	44.3
Penicillin	140.7	147.2	39.7

Notes: Hospitals making only one purchase during the period of study were excluded. The coefficient of variation is the ratio of the standard deviation to the mean.

of each product by the real price weighted with quantities for all purchases of the product. The formula for calculating the price index for each product is:

$$P^i_{t,h} = \frac{p^i_{t,h}}{\dfrac{\sum\limits_{t,h} p^i_{t,h} \cdot q^i_{t,h}}{\sum\limits_{t,h} q^i_{t,h}}}$$

[3.1]

where P is the weighted price index for product i in hospital h at time t; p is the real price paid; q is the quantity purchased. The price index will be greater than 1 when the real price of the product is greater than its average weighted price, and less than 1 otherwise.

A regression of this price index by purchase was constructed as an independent variable, against the quantities of each purchase.[12] An index to compare the quantities of different products purchased was also constructed for this variable. The index for each product is the relationship between the purchase quantity and the average purchase quantity, according to the following formula:

$$Q^i_{t,h} = \frac{q^i_{t,h}}{\dfrac{\sum\limits_{t,h} q^i_{t,h} \cdot q^i_{t,h}}{n^i}}$$

[3.2]

where Q is the quantity index for purchases of product i in hospital h at time t; q is the quantity purchased; n^i is the number of observations for each product. The quantity index is similar to the price index in that the index is greater than 1 when the purchase quantity is greater than the average quantity purchased of that product by all hospitals in the period of study, and less than 1 otherwise.

---

[12] Quantities are usually regarded as endogenous to prices in a context of demand and suply analysis. Endogeneity would lead to biased estimates of the coefficients. However, demand for inputs in public hospitals in Venezuela is almost uniquely driven by the supply of health care services by the hospital, which is in turn determined by demand. The quantity of inputs purchased is fixed by the demand of services to the hospital (which are provided for free), and thus exogenous to input prices.

Table 3.2 Price Variation across Hospitals, Controlling for Quantities

Variable	Regression 1		Regression 2	
Quantity	**-0.072**	*-3.88*	0.017	*0.78*
Constant	**1.21**	*44.63*		
Hospitals' fixed effects:				
1			**1.49**	*22.07*
2			**1.10**	*15.88*
3			**1.15**	*19.18*
5			**0.82**	*4.68*
6			**0.92**	*3.14*
7			**1.00**	*12.05*
8			**0.69**	*6.04*
9			**1.47**	*19.44*
10			**1.15**	*17.13*
11			**1.68**	*24.38*
12			**1.27**	*16.33*
13			**1.09**	*12.00*
14			**0.65**	*3.00*
15			**1.24**	*7.31*
16			**0.77**	*8.56*
17			**0.99**	*10.31*
18			**0.99**	*9.01*
19			**0.98**	*9.99*
20			**0.99**	*13.94*
21			**1.02**	*8.21*
22			**0.99**	*10.59*
N	249		249	
R^2	0.057		0.426	

Notes: The dependent variable is the price index described in the text. Quantity is the quantity index described in the text. The constant is excluded from the second regression because otherwise inclusion of all the hospital dummy variables would lead to linear dependency of the independent variables. Hospital 4 is omitted because it was not possible to obtain price information. Italics indicate t-statistics. Boldface indicates coefficients that are significant at the 10 percent level.

The results of Regression 1 show that the purchase quantities are significant in explaining the variations observed in prices (see Table 3.2). As expected, the quantities of each purchase (Q) have a significant inverse relationship with prices. Larger quantities are associated with lower unit prices. However the variations in quantities by themselves account for less than 6 percent of the price variation. When dummy variables are included to measure the fixed effects associated with each hospital, the quantity index loses its statistical significance (see Regression 2 in Table 3.2), and the explanatory power of the regression (as measured by the R^2) increases dramatically to 0.43. In sum, price variations are more strongly associated with differences between hospitals than with different purchase volumes.

The quantity index loses significance in Regression 2 because the index itself is strongly dependent on which hospital is involved. The quantity variations could be a consequence of a specific hospital characteristic, such as size, complexity, type, location, or volume of services offered. In fact, the quantities appear to be primarily a consequence of hospital size since the correlation between the quantity index and the number of beds per hospital is quite high (0.77). Consequently hospital size is an important control variable to include in any analysis of quantities or purchase prices.

In order to measure the impact of institutional design on the observed price variation, an index of purchase prices for each hospital, taking into account all of the products, was constructed for use as the dependent variable. The price indices for the four products are highly correlated (see Table 3.3), with one exception — cotton. The reason for this divergence is un-

Table 3.3 Price Correlations for Four Hospital Supplies

	Absorbent cotton	5% Dextrose solution	Penicillin	Normal saline solution
Absorbent cotton	1.00			
5% Dextrose solution	−0.02	1.00		
Penicillin	0.40	0.74	1.00	
Normal saline solution	−0.06	0.82	0.79	1.00

Notes: Statistically significant correlation coefficients are indicated in boldface. Definitions of the hospital supplies can be found in the text.

Table 3.4 Institutional Design and Control Factors, Indicators, and Sources

Factors	Indicators	Source
Control variables:		
Complexity and size of hospital	Number of beds	Information available in the hospital
Financial control	Delays in payment	Hospital records
Institutional variables:		
Probability of detection	Perception of the probability of detection	Survey
Probability of punishment	Perceived relationship between cases of punishment and the number of cases investigated.	Survey
Amount of penalty	Efficiency wage: difference between the salary of the hospital purchase manager and the opportunity cost in the labor market	Hospital records, and labor market information

Notes: Delays in payment are the average number of days the hospital takes to pay an invoice after receiving the merchandise. The efficiency wage represents the opportunity cost of the pay received in the current job compared with potential pay in the labor market. The shadow wage was calculated from a standard wage regression. Data from the Household Sampling Survey of 1995 (Central Office of Statistics and Informatics) in a national sample of 16,784 households was used to estimate the impact of educational level, years of experience, and gender on the wage of individuals receiving income. For the subjects of this study, the coefficients of this regression were used to estimate the salary that each person could expect based on their personal characteristics. The efficiency wage is the difference between this potential pay and the pay received by the employee in the hospital.

clear, so the subsequent analyses utilized two price indices. The first is a simple average of the price indices of the purchase prices for all products for each hospital; while the second is the same simple average, excluding cotton.

A regression model was constructed, with the price indices for each hospital as the dependent variable and the institutional variables as explanatory variables. These institutional design factors include the probability of detection and punishment, and the size of potential penalties. Two control variables were also included. The first controls for the effect of the size and

Table 3.5 Determinants of Purchase Prices across Hospitals

Variables	Price index excluding cotton				Price index including cotton			
Beds (x 10^{-3})	**-0.47**	*-2.05*	**-0.43**	*-2.37*	**-0.35**	*-1.85*	**-0.31**	*-2.00*
Delayed payment (days x 10^{-3})	3.70	*1.55*	-0.96	*-0.40*	1.10	*-0.66*	-1.10	*-0.77*
Perceived probability of detection (x 10^{-3})	1.40	*0.52*			1.50	*0.65*		
Efficiency wage of purchasing agent (x 10^{-7})	**3.42**	*2.08*			**2.34**	*1.71*		
Efficiency wage x probability of detection (x 10^{-9})			**6.44**	*2.21*			**4.66**	*1.96*
Constant	**1.07**	*6.42*	**1.27**	*9.43*	**1.09**	*8.16*	**1.21**	*11.60*
N	20		20		21			
Adj. R^2	0.32		0.30		0.16			0.20

Notes: Italics indicate t-statistics. Boldface indicates coefficients that are significant at the 10 percent level.

complexity of the hospital, and the second considers the possibility that the interhospital price variation is related to the cost of credit to suppliers. The independent variables of the regression are summarized in Table 3.4.

Table 3.5 presents the results of regressions using the two dependent variables (including and excluding cotton). The probability of punishment was not included among the independent variables of the regression because many hospitals reported no cases of investigating graft. Since the probability of sanction is conditional on detection, the nonexistence of detection in over 40 percent of the hospitals makes estimation of that effect impossible.

In both regressions, the estimated effects of the perceived probability of detection and delays in payment are not significant. It is unclear whether this is due to the absence of an effect or to problems in measurement. The perceived probability of detecting graft was derived from data that included many respondents who were not directly involved in the purchasing process (doctors, nurses, and service heads), and may have introduced measurement error. It is also possible that the specific form of asking the questions related to detection was flawed, and elicited confusing responses.

Figure 3.1 Price Index per Hospital by Delays in Payments

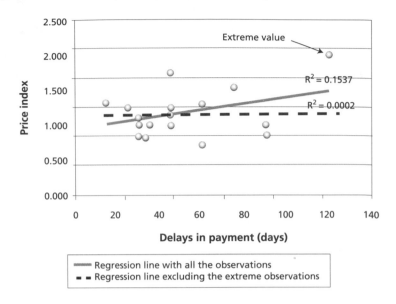

It is more puzzling that the delays in payment had no measurable impact, considering that the range for hospitals in the sample is between 15 and 120 days. During the first half of 1998, when the price information was recorded, annualized inflation was 32 percent and lending rates were above that value. Presumably differences in time of payment would have reflected the cost of money. Figure 3.1 shows that there is no such relationship after excluding one particular hospital, which had delayed payments on average for 120 days and had a price index almost double the average of the other hospitals. If this experience is set aside, there is no apparent relationship between credit and the interhospital price differences.

In Table 3.5, the estimated effect of hospital size (as measured by hospital beds) is significant, as expected from the previous results. Additionally, the amount of penalties is also a statistically significant explanatory factor for the price variation. When cotton prices are excluded, the results are even stronger, with an adjusted R^2 of 0.32. The signs of the coefficients are stable. There are no problems of heteroskedasticity, and the distribution of the residuals is normal. The sign of the variable for the volume of purchases by a hospital has the expected sign: the larger the volume of purchases, the lower the prices.

On the other hand the size of the penalty has an unexpected effect. The amount of the penalty is measured by the efficiency wage of the purchase manager; and the coefficient has a positive sign, indicating that when purchasing officers are more highly paid relative to alternative employment opportunities, the prices they pay for supplies are also higher.[13] This contradicts the initial hypothesis that a larger penalty would deter corruption.

One possible explanation for this surprising finding is related to the low probability of detection for this type of corruption. Compared with the other types of corruption, the perceived probability of detection is much lower on average for cases of graft (31.1 percent) than for theft or pilferage (47.8 percent) or absenteeism (72.1 percent). Furthermore the probability of punishment is so low that several sample hospitals have no records of penalties being applied for this type of infraction. Hence it was impossible to construct an adequate indicator of this factor. With a low probability of detection and a probability of punishment close to 0, the variables associated with the size of the penalty might not be able to deter corruption.

Another explanation could be that graft is susceptible to collusion between principals (hospital administrators) and agents (purchasing officers), especially in view of the close relationship between hospital directors and their purchase managers.[14] The positive correlation between the efficiency wage and overpaying for supplies could be the consequence of collusive agreements between the administrators and purchasers so as to extract income from the hospital. In other words, receiving an income above opportunity cost and benefiting from graft are both mechanisms that can be used to increase the income of corrupt agents.

Several pieces of evidence support this hypothesis. First, fewer than 15 percent of hospital directors agreed that graft takes place in public hospitals. Yet both the data on price dispersion and the perception of the other key interviewed informants, including the suppliers, show this type of corruption to be widespread in public hospitals.

---

[13] This result is maintained even when nominal pay replaces the efficiency wage as the independent variable.

[14] In a few cases, the hospital director was directly responsible for managing purchases. In such cases, the individual would be concerned only about being detected and penalized by authorities outside the hospital and thus be subject to less supervision than in cases where these two positions are held by distinct individuals.

Second, a positive relationship was found between the efficiency wage of the purchase manager and purchase prices. The theoretical model predicts a negative relationship: The higher the efficiency wage is, the higher the expected value of the penalty is, which should deter corruption. The positive correlation suggests that colluding principals and agents can use both wages and graft to extract income from the hospital.

To test this modified hypothesis the price index was regressed against the same control variables, but an additional explanatory variable was constructed and included, namely the probability of detection multiplied by the efficiency wage. The new variable is significant but, as with the efficiency wage in the previous regression, the estimated effect is the opposite of what one would expect (see Table 3.5).

The factors explaining the level of overpayment for supplies were expected to be the relative wage of the purchasing agent and the perceived probability of detection. However, these effects were not confirmed in the statistical analysis. In fact higher pay appears to be associated with higher, not lower, prices. This unexpected effect is even stronger when the wage is interacted with the perceived probability of detection.

One last possibility for explaining price variation could be the exercise of monopoly power by suppliers in the form of price discrimination. In such a case, suppliers would use their knowledge to charge higher prices to purchasers with inelastic demand than to those with more-elastic demand. However after controlling for the size and complexity of the hospital, the assumption of differences in the demand elasticity for inputs in the hospitals seems unsustainable. Moreover, price discrimination would not explain the difference in purchase prices for the same products in the same hospital.

Institutional Incentives and Overpayment

As noted above, the findings could be due to collusion or poor measures of the penalty (possible loss of pay) and the probability of detection (based on perceptions). If the latter is true, it should be possible to construct other measures, based on institutional design, that are important in determining the perceived probability of detection. These institutional factors should be related to the supervisor's capacity to supervise the agents' actions.

To test this hypothesis, an index was constructed to measure the degree of hierarchical control within the hospital. This index was constructed using the answers to questions regarding: the social acceptance of graft among peers, lax procurement procedures, the existence of historical price controls, the number of audits per year, and community participation in hospital management.[15]

However, internal controls are only effective if there is no collusion between the hospital administration and the purchasing officer. Hence it is also necessary to consider mechanisms that hold the hospital administration accountable, that is, external controls. Therefore an external control index was also constructed. At this point in the agent-principal chain, the director is the agent, and the level to which he or she reports is the principal.[16] The external control index was built using answers regarding the existence of: accountability for how user fees are applied; discretionary authority for hospital directors in the allocation of surplus resources; explicit criteria for appointment of the director; multiple mandates (several principals); and the number of agency relationships between the hospital director and the local community.

If hospital directors have the right incentives, they will establish internal controls and incentives that increase the likelihood of detection (or perceived probability of detection). Thus the perceived probability of detection should be positively correlated with the two control indices (internal and external).

The correlation between the external and internal controls, although low, is positive as expected (see Table 3.6). This confirms that hospitals with

---

[15] The answer to each question was normalized to be of a value between 0 and 1, with 1 meaning the highest hierarchical control and 0 the lowest. For example, in the case of "social acceptance of grafts among peers" the number assigned to a hospital is the proportion of people within the hospital that regarded grafts as unacceptable behavior. The variable "existence of historical price controls" is dichotomous with value 1 if controls exist in the hospital and 0 if they don't. The variable "number of audits per year" is the number of audits the hospital went through divided by the maximum number of audits reported by any of the hospitals in the sample. Again, the hospitals with the maximum number of audits in the sample have a value of 1 in this variable, and hospitals with no audits have a value of 0. And so on with the rest of the questions. The control index is just the average of each of these variables, which also leads to a normalized index of control between 0 and 1, with 1 being the maximum control. The same procedure was followed for the calculation of each of the indices of control used.

[16] Although this new level may also be involved in charging commissions for purchases, it is not our focus.

Table 3.6 Relationship Between Control and Detection (correlation coefficient)

	Probability of detection	Internal control index	External control index
Probability of detection	1.00		
Internal control index	−0.27	1.00	
External control index	−0.13	0.11	1.00

better external controls also have better internal controls. Yet expectation about the primary concern — the effect of controls on the perceived probability of detection — is not borne out. In fact, the results show the correlation to be low and negative. This finding raises doubts about the quality of the information in the perceived-probability-of-detection variable. In the hope that the control indices might be better indicators of the likelihood of being caught, the regressions in Table 3.5 were reestimated after substituting the internal and external control indices for the perceived probability of detection. However, once again the coefficients of these variables were not statistically significant explanations for the price differences.

Determinants of Supply Theft

Theft appears to be widespread in public hospitals. When key informants were asked about the frequency of pilferage in their facilities, more than half indicated that surgical supplies, medicine, and equipment have been stolen (see Table 3.7). Asked to assess the volume of supplies stolen, they estimated the loss at about 10 percent.

To analyze the determinants of theft, an index was created that combined these two sets of responses as variables. The index specifically multiplied the proportion of people who acknowledged cases of pilferage in the hospital (of surgical supplies, medicines, equipment, food, and others), by the reported share of supplies stolen. Such an index is not a precise measure of the magnitude and frequency of theft, but it should be a good proxy for the general level of theft.

Table 3.7 Measures of Theft in Public Hospitals

	Share stating that theft occurs (%)	Share of supplies stolen (%)
Surgical supplies	67.0	10.1
Medicines	64.4	13.4
Equipment	50.1	5.7
Food	42.3	12.2
Others	28.2	3.4

Source: Survey of hospital staff.

The explanatory variables are shown in Table 3.8. The amount of the penalty is approximated by the difference between the levels of pay in the hospital relative to the expected salary that people with similar skills are earning in the labor market. The *expected* value of the penalty adjusts this difference for the average time an individual would be unemployed before obtaining a new job. It also adjusts for the probability that punishment by hospital authorities will be applied. Since the expected value of the penalty is, in part, a function of the perceived probability of sanctions, these two variables are not used together in the same regression (the simple correlation between both variables is 0.56).

Both variables were constructed with the weighted average pay of doctors, graduate and auxiliary nurses, and those workers who are in most frequent contact with the supplies, medicines, and other materials and equipment between delivery to the hospital and final use.

Two regressions were then estimated, differing only in two included variables (see Table 3.9). In both regressions, the *potential benefits* (as indicated by hospital size) are highly significant (at the 1 percent level). The more beds there are, the larger the hospital is, and the higher the reported amount of theft. The *reported probability of detection* is also statistically significant (at the 1 percent level) in both regressions. In hospitals with a higher perceived probability of detection, the reported amount of theft appears to be lower.

The variable measuring the probability of punishment being applied was small and statistically insignificant. Additionally the value of the pen-

Table 3.8 Explanatory Factors, Indicators, and Information Sources for the Study of Theft

Factors	Indicators	Sources
Expected benefit	Number of beds (size of hospital): larger hospitals with a higher volume of services provide more opportunities for pilferage and higher potential benefit. This variable is also associated with the probability of detection because supervision and control is more difficult and costly in larger hospitals. However the relationship is modified by the existence of control mechanisms. Under both interpretations, the expected effect on the dependant variable is the same: pilferage increases with the number of beds (increase in expected benefit and/or reduction in the probability of detection).	Hospital records and secondary sources
Probability of detection	Perceived probability of detection among hospital employees.	Survey
Probability of punishment	Reported relationship between cases investigated and cases resulting in penalties.	Survey
Amount of penalty	Average efficiency wages of doctors, nurses, and workers, weighted by the number of each staff type in the hospital.	Available information and authors' calculations
Expected value of penalty	Calculated as the opportunity cost of the different types of penalties applied to theft in each hospital multiplied by the reported frequency distribution of each type of penalty. The opportunity cost is calculated as the weighted average pay for each staff type.	Available information and authors' calculations.

alty, as measured by the weighted average efficiency wage, appears to have no impact on the amount of pilferage in either specification. Despite this, the *expected value* of the penalty — the product of the probability of being punished and the potential loss of income — is statistically significant at the 10 percent level. This indicates that the expected penalty has a small negative impact on theft. Both regressions explain nearly two-thirds of the variation in the index of theft. The coefficients are stable; there are no problems of heteroskedasticity or autocorrelation; and the errors follow a normal distribution.

Table 3.9 Regressions across Hospitals for Variations in Theft

	(1)		(2)	
Hospital beds	**0.15**	*4.66*	**0.013**	*4.26*
Reported probability of detection	**−0.13**	*−2.79*	**−0.12**	*−2.44*
Exp. amt. of penalty (coef. x 10⁻⁶)	−1.80*	*−1.76*		
Reported probability of sanction			0.23	*0.072*
Average efficiency wage in the hospital (coef. x 10⁻⁶)	6.62	*1.31*	−0.445	*−0.12*
Constant	**9.96**	*3.62*	**8.55**	*2.96*
Observations	21		22	
Adj. R²	0.67		0.61	

Notes: Italics indicate t-statistics. Boldface indicates statistically significant at the 5 percent level, and (*) indicates statistically significant at the 10 percent level.

Institutional Incentives and Theft

The reported probability of discovering thefts should be affected by the principal's capacity to obtain information on agents' conduct. As with the analysis of overpayment, an internal control index was constructed. This index combined the following variables: social acceptance of theft by peers, use of an historical record for supply control, ex post audits comparing supplies used to services provided, community participation in hospital management, and size and complexity of the hospital (number of beds).[17]

These internal controls are expected to increase both the probability that theft will be discovered and measurement accuracy of what and how much is stolen. In fact, the perceived probability of detection is positively correlated with the control index. The probability of detection explains about 17 percent of the variation in the perceived probability of detection between hospitals, and is statistically significant at the 10 percent level.

The perceived probability of detection should also be affected by the principal's capacity to enforce penalties effectively. Again, we constructed

---

[17] See footnote 15 for more details.

an index, this time of the hospital's ability to apply sanctions when theft is discovered. The index used two variables: the ability of unions and professional organizations to influence hospital human resource policy and the directors' independence (from higher levels) in the management of human resources. A regression of the perceived probability of penalties being applied on the ability-to-punish index confirms that there is a positive relationship. The institutional factors account for almost 15 percent of the variation across hospitals in the perceived probability of punishment.

Determinants of Absenteeism

Key informants highlighted staff absenteeism as a serious problem that affects hospitals' ability to provide timely and good quality services. However, the characteristics and determinants of absenteeism are not the same for all personnel levels. In particular, absenteeism of doctors, professional nurses, and auxiliary nurses must be studied separately because their contracts, options for alternative employment, and degrees of supervision differ significantly.

In general, the systems of hiring and pay for doctors and nurses are very different. The peculiarities of the labor market in the public and private sectors also generate variations in mobility between sectors for both types of personnel, which could affect their opportunity costs. More specifically:

- ♦ The wage differential between the public and private sectors for the three types of personnel varies, especially between doctors and nurses. The relationship between doctors' average wages in the private and public sectors (calculated from the sample) is 4.5, while the ratio for graduate nurses is 0.99, and for auxiliary nurses, 1.03. Clearly doctors face a much greater incentive to dedicate time to activities outside the public hospital.

- ♦ Doctors face strong barriers to entry into private clinics. The most frequent mechanism for acquiring the right to work in a private clinic is through owning a share in the clinic, whose cost varies considerably but averages about two-and-a-half years' pay for a doctor in the private sector. The other option, less frequent, is approval by the clinic board, which is usually associated with a doctor's reputation and skill, professional status, and social relations with the clinic's doctors and management team.

♦ Nurses, on the other hand, face strong barriers to entry into public hospitals. In fact the hiring of professional nurses in public hospitals depends, in most cases, on a selection process that is supposed to be competitive but that is not always transparent, according to some of the nurses in the survey.

From the survey, it appears that absenteeism differed significantly between nurses and doctors. Table 3.10 shows a comparison of absenteeism by staff category, measured by responses to the questionnaire regarding the share of contracted hours that go unworked. The highest rates were for staff least likely to be supervised, that is, for doctors and head nurses (reportedly absent 37 percent and 30 percent of their contracted hours, respectively). Residents and nurses are also absent a substantial amount of time, but not nearly as much — missing 8 percent to between 9 and 14 percent of their contracted hours, respectively.

A second factor that encourages or discourages absenteeism is the potential cost of being dismissed. For example, residents need to work in public hospitals in order to gain experience, particularly if they are studying to become specialists. Their postgraduate performance depends explicitly on their attendance and work in the hospital. Consequently it is not surprising to see that residents are least likely to be absent — even less than professional nurses.

Table 3.10 Reported Absentee Rates of Hospital Staff by Job Classification (percent of contracted hours missed)

Type of staff	Average hours absent	Standard deviation
Resident doctors	7.5	7.1
Specialists	35.9	17.7
Head nurses	29.8	19.7
Professional nurses	9.7	6.9
Auxiliary nurses	13.6	7.0

Table 3.11 Explanatory Factors, Indicators, and Sources for Variations in Absenteeism

Factors	Indicators	Sources
Probability of detection	Personnel's perceived probability of being detected for absenteeism.	Survey
Probability of sanction	Personnel's perceived probability of penalty enforcement, calculated as the relationship between the perceptions of the number of cases of penalties and the number of cases investigated or detected.	Survey
Amount of the penalty and expected benefit	Efficiency wage of each personnel type: difference between pay and opportunity cost.	Survey and authors' calculations
Expected value of the penalty	Calculated as the opportunity cost of the different types of penalties applied to absenteeism in each hospital, multiplied by the frequency distribution of each type of penalty. The opportunity cost is calculated from the pay of each type of personnel.	Survey and authors' calculations

To analyze these hypotheses empirically, an absenteeism index was constructed for the reported share of time missed by each type of personnel. The index utilized information from two questions: one related to the share of days that staff were present and one related to the share of hours that staff were present on any given day. Subtracting the product of these two ratios from one yields an estimate of the time that staff were absent from the hospital.[18]

The explanatory factors that were analyzed are shown in Table 3.11. The characteristics of the variables are the same as those discussed in relation to theft. The expected income from a corrupt act is associated with the value of free time or the expected pay from alternative employment. The value of free time is not measured in this research, and the expected pay from an alternative job is incorporated in the calculation of the efficiency wage.

---

[18] For more details, see Jaén and Paravisini (1999).

In the analysis, the efficiency wage reflects both the potential loss of income if dismissed and the expected income (from being absent and working elsewhere). Other things being equal, a higher efficiency wage indicates a larger penalty and less potential benefit from alternative use of time. Thus, in both situations, higher efficiency wages will be associated with lower levels of absenteeism. Absenteeism is also expected to be higher in hospitals where the probabilities of detection and punishment are lower (e.g., larger hospitals).

Table 3.12 presents the regressions for absenteeism among doctors and professional nurses. The regressions for auxiliary nurses are not included because none of the explanatory variables proved significant in their case.

The perceived probability of detection and the efficiency wage are significant in explaining variations in doctors' absenteeism. Absenteeism increases among doctors when the probability of detection decreases. It also increases when the size of the expected penalty decreases and when potential earnings in alternative employment increase. Nevertheless, the perceived probability of sanctions being applied and the amount of the penalty are not statistically significant. Still, the significant variables have the expected sign and account for about 27 percent of the variation in absenteeism among doctors.

Table 3.12 Determinants of Absenteeism and Medical Leaves by Personnel Type

	Doctors' absenteeism		Professional nurses			
			Absenteeism		Medical leave	
Reported probability of detection (coef. x 10^{-3})	**−7.20**	*−2.40*	**−2.20**	*−1.80*	**0.0023**	*1.98*
Reported probability of penalty for absenteeism	0.02	*0.15*	**−0.12**	*−2.44*	−0.035	*−0.70*
Expected penalty (coef. x 10^{-7})	**−1.02**	*−1.46*	**−0.67**	*−1.88*	0.12	*0.33*
Efficiency wage (coef. x 10^{-7})	**1.26**	*1.73*	2.07	*0.60*	1.95	*0.44*
Constant	**0.96**	*4.12*	**0.33**	*3.33*	−0.096	*−0.99*
Observations	22		22		20	
Adj. R^2	0.27		0.28		0.015	

Notes: Italics indicate t-statistics. Boldface indicates statistically significant at the 10 percent level.

Among professional nurses, the probability of detection, probability of punishment, and the expected penalty are all statistically significant in explaining absenteeism, and they have the expected signs. By contrast the efficiency wage is not significant in the regression, indicating that pay is not an important explanatory factor for absenteeism at this staff level. The regression explains almost 28 percent of the variation in professional nurses' absenteeism.

As previously noted, nurses have low absentee rates relative to head nurses and doctors. Yet key informants indicated that nursing staff might be using medical leave, which is intended only for reasons of illness, to take time off even when the leave taker is well. This perception is quite widespread. To evaluate this possibility empirically, we regressed medical leaves against the various institutional factors associated with corruption. If medical leaves were requested only for reasons of illness, then presumably they would not be associated with the factors identified in the absenteeism model.

The last two columns of Table 3.12 show a regression of average number of days per month in which medical leave was requested per nurse in each hospital, using the same factors that were used to explain absenteeism. The regression does not provide any firm statistical evidence about the hypothesis of abuse since it explains very little of the variation in days of medical leave per nurse. The only statistical indication that medical leaves are affected by the same factors that influence absenteeism is the probability of detection, which is statistically significant at the 10 percent level and which is, unexpectedly, positive. That is, in the hospitals where the probability of detection of absenteeism is higher, nurses make more intensive use of medical leave.

This finding highlights one of the difficulties involved in measuring illegal activities that affect services: people are highly inventive, and adjust to different contexts. Perhaps nurses in hospitals where supervision is stronger rely on medical leaves to get their "time off" instead of simply not showing up. Getting a medical leave differs from unjustified absence because it is recorded, and involves certain costs associated with obtaining the justification. On the other hand, personnel can use it as a device to reduce the probability of being detected for unjustified absence. This interpretation is supported by the fact that personnel do not perceive *justified* medical leave as absenteeism.[19]

---

[19] Information obtained from interviews of hospital directors and key informants.

Institutional Incentives and Absenteeism

As in the cases of overpayment and theft, the study looked for aspects of institutional design that influence the factors affecting absenteeism. In particular, an association is expected between the probability of detection and the supervisory capacity of the hospital director over personnel. To establish this relationship, a control index was constructed from the following institutional indicators:

♦ *Total number of hospital personnel.* This is an indicator of the costs and complexity associated with personal supervision. As the number of personnel increases, the exercise of supervision and control becomes more difficult and costly. Therefore the perceived probability of detection is lower.

♦ *Social acceptance of corruption.* The greater the social acceptance of absenteeism by peers, the lower the probability of detection.

♦ *Existence of mechanisms to measure performance.* These mechanisms increase the probability of detection. If the hospital director has mechanisms to measure staff performance, the agents' perceived probability of detection should also rise.

♦ *Community participation in hospital management.* The expected behavior is similar to the previous case, but the population acts as the principal.

In fact this control index is highly correlated with the perceived probability of detection, with a correlation coefficient of 0.51. Another way of seeing this relationship is to regress the perceived probability of detection against the control index. When this is done, the control index alone explains more than 25 percent of the variation across hospitals in the perceived probability of detection.

The perceived probability of punishment should also be associated with the effective capacity of the principals to apply sanctions. To quantify the capacity to apply sanctions, an enforcement capacity index was constructed, based on the hospital director's independence in hiring and dismissing personnel and the influence of unions and professional organizations over human resources management. The correlation between the perceived probability of punishment and the capacity to enforce penalties is 0.13. This correlation is positive as expected, but not statistically strong.

Conclusions and Policy Recommendations

In surveys and interviews, three types of corruption were reported to be common in the public hospitals in Venezuela: graft in purchasing medical supplies; theft or pilferage of supplies and medicines; and absenteeism among doctors and nurses. Looking at these illegal activities through a traditional model of criminal behavior and agency theory has allowed us to evaluate the impact of institutional design on the extent of corruption. In particular, the probability of detection and punishment appeared to play a large role in explaining theft and absenteeism. In turn, the probabilities of detection and punishment appear to be associated with the existence of administrative controls and with independent management of human resources by the hospital director, respectively. By contrast, pay levels did not appear to have any impact on theft and, if anything, were associated with higher prices paid for supply purchases. Because the simple agency model was unable to explain differences in overpayment, it may be necessary to develop a more sophisticated model of illegal behavior that would incorporate the possibility of collusion between administrators and their staff.

Graft and Overpayments

There was considerable dispersion in purchase prices of homogeneous products, both between hospitals and between purchases in the same hospital; and these differences persist even after controlling for discounts and financial surcharges related to quantities and credit terms, and for differences between administrative purchasing procedures.[20] This finding was interpreted as evidence confirming the views of key informants that graft was common in purchases made by public hospitals.

The factors that were expected to be associated empirically with overpayment were generally statistically insignificant. There are a number of pos-

---

[20] The selection of the sample in a relatively restricted geographical area meant that control for distance from suppliers was unnecessary.

sible explanations for this. First, the specification should have included a variable representing the perceived probability of penalties being applied. However this probability is conditional on detecting corruption, and in over 40 percent of the hospitals no cases of overpayment had been detected or prosecuted.

Second, the variable for probability of detection may be unreliable. This variable was based on the perceptions of key informants who may not possess sufficient or direct information about the purchasing process.

Third, the probabilities of detection and punishment for graft are much lower than for other types of corruption. Since the expected penalty is based on the multiplication of these probabilities by the amount of the penalty, the expected influence over agents' conduct may be insignificant.

Based on interviews with key informants, it is possible that the poor statistical findings are due to the existence of collusion between the principals and agents involved in the purchasing process. Hospital directors, who have the capacity to supervise agents and establish internal controls and incentives, are closely involved in the procurement process. In fact, in many of the cases studied, the hospital director is directly responsible for purchases.

If this is the case, then institutional reforms for reducing graft should focus on the hospital's external incentives. One such arrangement would be to introduce an element of competition for the resources that are transferred to the hospital. As long as the resources for purchases come from unconditional historical transfers, the hospital's administrators and purchasing agents have little incentive to seek the lowest price. This situation is aggravated when hospital performance is not measured by results or productivity but only by budget execution.

Theft

Theft is another form of illegal activity reported to be common in public hospitals. More than 50 percent of the key informants admit knowing about cases of pilferage in hospitals, and the estimated loss from stealing is generally higher than 10 percent of surgical supplies and medicines.

Statistical analysis shows that pilferage increases when the potential benefit from theft is high, when the probability of detection is low, and when the expected amount of the penalty (value of the penalty multiplied by probability of punishment) is also low. This analysis confirmed the theoretical model, with one exception: the level of theft does not appear to be affected by wages. That is, theft in public hospitals appears to be more closely related to the probabilities of detection and punishment than to levels of pay.

Management and supply controls are significant in explaining different perceptions of the probability of detecting theft across hospitals. Similarly the capacity of hospital principals to apply penalties is positively correlated with the perceived probability of punishment as reported in the surveys. Thus the evidence supports the expectation that perceptions of the probability of detection and sanction respond to specific incentives related to the hospital's institutional design.

These results suggest that introducing or reinforcing internal control could reduce hospital theft. Such systems include inventory control — from the moment supplies enter the hospital until they are used in service provision. They also rely on users participating in hospital management and oversight. Finally, institutional frameworks that encourage peer control can also reduce pilferage. For example, the cost of missing supplies can be charged to all members of the responsible group.

Another way to decrease theft is to enhance the enforcement capacity of hospital principals by reducing or eliminating the influence of unions and professional organizations over human resources policy. By strengthening the hospital director's capacity to manage human resources with less interference, it would be easier for penalties to be meted out in cases of proven theft. This, in turn, would increase the perceived probability of punishment among hospital personnel.

Absenteeism

Absenteeism is also reported to be common in Venezuela's public hospitals. It appears to be more frequent among doctors and head nurses than among staff nurses or medical residents. The estimated proportion of contracted hours that are not worked by the doctors and head nurses is 36 percent and 30 percent, respectively. For medical residents, professional nurses, and auxiliary nurses the proportion of absences is about 7 percent, 9 percent, and 13 percent, respectively.

The only explanatory variable that was significant in explaining absenteeism among both specialist doctors and professional nurses is the probability of detection. For both types of personnel, an increase in the perceived probability of detection is associated with an increase in compliance with contracted hours. For doctors, higher pay relative to their remunerative opportunities from alternative uses of time is associated with a lower rate of absenteeism. Absenteeism among professional nurses appears to be lower whenever the probability of penalties being applied is higher and when the expected penalty is larger.

Differences in the behavior of both types of personnel are probably due to the specific characteristics of their respective job markets. For example, the ratio between average pay in the public and private sectors is 4.5 for doctors and close to 1.0 for nurses. Moreover there are strong entry barriers for doctors who want to work in private clinics, while nurses face barriers to working in public hospitals.

Another factor that can influence nurses is their ability to use medical leaves instead of unjustified absences. Evidence was found that average monthly hours of medical leave among nurses are positively associated with the probability of detection. That is, nurses use medical leave more intensively in hospitals where the perceived probability of detecting absenteeism is higher.

Analysis of the various institutional mechanisms for controlling absenteeism shows they have an impact on the perceived probability of detection and a positive, but statistically insignificant, impact on the perceived probability of punishment. This implies that institutional control mechanisms can be effective, but one size will not fit all. The results demonstrate that the empirical determinants of absenteeism are different for nurses and doctors, and policies should be designed accordingly for each personnel type.

To bolster in-hospital influence over doctors' absenteeism, the principal's supervisory capacity needs to be reinforced. This requires, among other things, a system of internal controls designed to raise the perceived probability of detection, namely: increased peer control, introduction of mechanisms to measure performance, and community involvement in management. Consideration should also be given to the level of doctors' pay in public hospitals. As previously noted, doctors' pay is over four times higher in the private than in the public sector. A policy to increase the remuneration of medical personnel could be effective, but to achieve the expected results it would have to be accompanied by policies that increase the probability that penalties will be applied in cases of absenteeism.

Similarly, reduced absenteeism among professional nurses requires reinforcement of the principal's supervisory capacity by giving the director greater ability to apply penalties. This requires limiting the power of unions and professional organizations in personnel decisions so that hospital directors can manage their staff more effectively.

A Note to Policymakers

This chapter has studied the determinants of corrupt practices in Venezuela's public hospitals and the design of policies to combat them. Since the corrupt practices studied were selected because of their impact on efficiency, it is hoped that implementing such policies would lead to a more efficient use of scarce hospital resources and thereby improve public services.

However not all policies that reduce illegal activities will improve efficiency. Corrupt practices are sometimes how agents adapt their conduct to distortions introduced by institutional restrictions, whose modification is outside the competence of hospital managers and directors. Some of these distortions can be found in the design of the financing system, the legal regulations that govern human resources management, and the centralization of budgetary decisions.

For example, absenteeism among specialist doctors can be a means of adjusting real wages per hour since nominal wages are centrally fixed by other government agencies. If this mechanism did not exist, the low level of doctors' real wages in public hospitals would create a shortage of qualified medical personnel, with negative consequences for health services.

Consequently, it is important not to lose sight of the effects on the efficiency, effectiveness, and equity of health care when designing policies to reduce corruption. To eliminate corruption is not an end in itself but a means to increase the productivity, quality, and coverage of public hospital services.

CHAPTER 4

Transparency and Accountability in Argentina's Hospitals

*Ernesto Schargrodsky, Jorge Mera, and
Federico Weinschelbaum*

The 33 public hospitals of the City Government of Buenos Aires (CGBA) purchase their inputs through a decentralized process. In September 1996, the CGBA Health Secretariat implemented a policy of monitoring purchase prices. This chapter uses the database generated by this policy to analyze two related questions — what is the impact of monitoring on prices and what is the effect of purchasing managers' wages on prices. Results show that the policy did lower prices but the transitory effect was stronger than the permanent one, suggesting that transparency is not a sufficient deterrent against corruption unless accompanied by some form of penalty. Contrary to expectations, the purchasing managers' wages, relative to their expected earnings in the labor market, were not associated with lower purchase prices. The chapter also discusses survey results identifying absenteeism as the most serious form of abuse by doctors and nurses in public hospitals.

Introduction

Public hospitals are subject to corruption, with public funds diverted to obtain private benefits.[1] Such corruption can be particularly damaging to society for several reasons. First, even a low incidence of corruption is costly because of the large volume of resources allocated to this sector. In 1995,

---

[1] Although there is no consensus on its definition (Palmier, 1983; Johnston, 1997), corruption is usually considered to be the use of public office by state officials for their own benefit (Shleifer and Vishny, 1993; OAS, 1996; Bardhan, 1997).

expenditure on public hospitals in Argentina was 1.3 percent of GDP (González García and Tobar, 1997).[2] Second, diversion of health funds harms social equity. In Argentina, health spending has a more redistributive impact than most other public outlays (Diéguez et al., 1990). Third, public hospital corruption cannot be attacked simply by reducing government participation in the sector. Agreement on the need for State financing and delivery of health services is based not only on the previously cited grounds of social equity (extending services to needy sectors of society), but also on economic efficiency (the existence of strong externalities since it is in each individual's self-interest to have healthy neighbors). Furthermore it is well known that a purely private solution is not feasible because private provision of health services suffers from numerous agency problems (Arrow, 1963; Feldstein, 1993).

Varied opportunities for corruption are easy to imagine in public hospitals. Corrupt practices may exist in the procurement processes for food, janitorial, and security services; staff appointments; absenteeism during working hours; use of supplies, facilities, and labor resources for personal benefit; improper referral of patients to private practices; improper billing of patients; and graft for purchases of equipment and inputs.

This chapter examines subjective evidence on some forms of corruption in public hospitals, drawing on data obtained from surveys of doctors, nurses, and patients[3] in three public hospitals and one private hospital in the city of Buenos Aires.

The chapter also uses hard data to focus on another dimension of hospital corruption: graft in purchasing supplies for hospitals of the Government of the City of Buenos Aires (CGBA). The 33 hospitals of the CGBA health system purchase their inputs under a decentralized system. Each hospital has its own purchasing office, headed by a purchasing manager. In September 1996, in an innovative effort to increase transparency in purchasing procedures, the CGBA Health Secretariat, through the Subsecretariat of Strategic Management, ordered all the hospitals under its jurisdiction to report the prices paid for a range of inputs. Beginning in October 1996, the com-

---

[2] The actual percentage is larger since this figure excludes expenditures in institutions belonging to the social security system, some of which are also administered by the State.

[3] For the purposes of this paper, the term "patients" refers to people who received treatment at the four hospitals or, in the case of children and those too infirm to participate, the family member who accompanied the patient to treatment.

piled information was sent regularly to all the hospitals in a form that high-lighted the institutions that had paid the highest and lowest prices for each item.

Through this monitoring policy, the Secretariat compiled a database for the purchases made by the hospitals between August 1996 and December 1997. This makes it possible to study a unique set of objective microeconomic data, and is a contribution to the existing literature on corruption compiled from surveys (Ades and Di Tella, 1995, 1997a; Mauro, 1995; Kaufmann and Wei, 1999).

The price data also allows one to test whether the "efficiency wages" of CGBA purchase managers affect purchase prices. An efficiency wage is the difference between an agent's nominal wage and what a person with similar characteristics would earn in an average job elsewhere in the economy. This difference represents the magnitude of what the individual purchasing agent risks losing if he or she were to be found unsatisfactory and dismissed. Presumably, higher efficiency wages should induce workers to be more attentive to the principal's interest in productivity (Yellen, 1984; Shapiro and Stiglitz, 1984). Van Rijckeghem and Weder (1997) explicitly consider the hypothesis that higher wages in the civil service are associated with less corruption, and find confirmation in cross-country evidence. Such an argument would indicate that public hospitals with well-paid purchasing managers should be paying less for supplies. In fact, the empirical evidence in this chapter shows that efficiency wages have no statistically significant effect on supply purchase prices. The difference in findings from Van Rijckeghem and Weder may be because the data sources in this chapter are more specific (limited to public hospitals) and more objective (recorded price data).

Public hospitals in Argentina are by no means the only public entities susceptible to corruption. Doctors, nurses, and patients believe that corruption in public hospitals is no more serious than in the rest of society. That is, they tend to consider public hospitals to be either as corrupt as or less corrupt than other parts of society (see Table 4.1).

Overview of CGBA Public Hospitals

The CGBA public hospital system is the largest municipal hospital system in Argentina and is surpassed in size only by the network of Buenos Aires Prov-

Table 4.1 Perception of Corruption in Public Hospitals vs. Rest of Society (In percent)

Level	Doctors	Nurses	Patients
Higher	3.7	13.2	12.9
Equal	72.6	52.0	45.2
Lower	23.5	34.6	41.9

Notes: The survey methodology is described in the text. The question was: "Is corruption in public hospitals more, equal, or less than in other areas of society?"

ince. In the city of Buenos Aires, the CGBA is the leading health care provider, delivering services to the inhabitants of the city, the suburbs, and even beyond. The CGBA is by far the largest hospital manager. Although private-sector facilities have more hospital beds in total, they are dispersed among many independent facilities (see Table 4.2).

Within the extensive hospital network operated by the CGBA Health Secretariat, there is a range of institutional complexity (see Table 4.3). There are 29 hospitals (13 general care, 2 children's general care, and 14 specialized) that offer in-patient treatment, 3 dental service centers (2 for adults

Table 4.2 Hospital Beds — City of Buenos Aires (1995)

Institution	Beds
CGBA	8,375
Social works	1,679
Private sector	10,307
University	950
Armed forces	843
Security forces	390
National and mixed	508
Total	23,052

Source: CGBA Health Secretariat (1997b).

Table 4.3 Characteristics of CGBA Hospitals (1997)

Type	Number
General	13
Pediatric	2
Specialized	14
Maternity	(1)
Infectious disease	(1)
Oncology	(1)
Ophthalmology	(?)
Burns	(1)
Gastroenterology	(1)
Mental health	(4)
Rehabilitation	(3)
Dental	3
Zoonosis	1
Total	33

Source: CGBA Health Secretariat (1997b).

and 1 for children) that offer only outpatient care, and a zoonosis institute.[4]

Survey Results of Hospital Doctors, Nurses, and Patients

To obtain information about the public hospitals of the city of Buenos Aires, surveys were conducted in four facilities.[5] Respondents were queried about their perceptions of illegal activity in their facilities, which were selected to cover a range of ownership or managerial forms. They included (1) an autonomous hospital, which was a mixed self-managed pediatric establishment financed by CGBA and the national government, (2) a nonprofit private hospital, which provided general services and was operated by a nonprofit

---

[4] In a broad sense, we refer to all these institutions as "hospitals." The system also has 30 health centers and a modality for general practitioners.

[5] For reasons of confidentiality, the names of the institutions are not provided.

organization, and (3) CGBA1 and CGBA2, which were two general hospitals in the city government system.

The surveys of doctors, nurses, and outpatients were taken between October and November 1998. A simple random sample was used, aiming for 30 interviewees for each category in each participating establishment. Potential interviewees in the different hospital departments were invited to respond voluntarily to the survey. This was the preferred method for doctors and nurses instead of a random draw from the list of employees. This was done to strengthen participants' confidence in the anonymity of the survey. The patients themselves or their accompanying family members were interviewed after treatments were given. This criterion was used to ensure that the respondents could better evaluate service delivery.[6]

Perceptions of Absenteeism

The survey's first section asked questions about absenteeism among doctors, distinguishing absent days from cases in which doctors report for work but fail to complete their full shifts. Combining both should cover the overall level of absenteeism in each hospital, as perceived by the respondents.

The combined total calculated in this way is considerable. On average, doctors who responded to the questionnaire estimated doctor absenteeism rates of 19 percent for any given 20-day work period. According to nurses, doctor absenteeism averaged about 32 percent (see Table 4.4).[7] In response to other questions, doctors, and to a lesser extent nurses, stated that doctors are absent less frequently than are nurses and administrative personnel. Thus, the problem of absenteeism may be even more severe among the rest of the hospital staff. In the public hospitals, this level of absenteeism represents an important loss of resources since personnel expenses absorb 69.8 percent of the CGBA health budget (Mera et al., 1999). In contrast to the public hospitals, there appears to be significantly less absenteeism in the private hospital.

---

[6] The forms used and additional details are given in Mera et al. (1999).

[7] Of the doctors and nurses who answered that there was no absenteeism among doctors, 30.3 percent and 27.7 percent, respectively, gave a positive reply when asked about its causes. This contradiction suggests that the estimates of absenteeism may understate the problem. The percentage of contradictions was higher in the private hospital.

Table 4.4 Perceived Absenteeism by Doctors: Share of Weekly Workload (In percent)

Respondents:	Absences during some part of the day		Absences for an entire day		Total absenteeism	
	Doctors	Nurses	Doctors	Nurses	Doctors	Nurses
Hospitals						
Hospital 1	13.3	22.9	5.5	13.8	18.8	36.7
Hospital 2	7.8	5.8	1.4	7.0	9.1	12.8
Hospital 3	15.8	24.6	4.2	10.8	20.0	35.4
Hospital 4	20.8	27.6	6.7	16.4	27.5	44.0
All	14.5	20.2	4.5	12.0	19.0	32.1

Notes: The questions asked were: "In general, for every 8 hours contracted, how many does a typical doctor effectively work in your hospital?" and "In general, for every 20 working days, how many does a typical doctor work in your hospital?" The percentages in the table represent the average of the responses of those surveyed.

Except in the nonprofit private hospital, the amount of doctor hourly absenteeism reported by the nursing staff is higher than that declared by the doctors themselves. This holds true for all causes and all three public hospitals. Both doctors and nurses agree that hourly absenteeism is more common than missed days. Patients' perspectives on levels of absenteeism among doctors were similar to the views expressed by personnel. On average, 23.2 percent of patients agreed that "the doctors in this hospital do not respect working hours." This figure was 26.9 percent and 29.2 percent in the CGBA hospitals, respectively, 18.2 percent in the autonomous hospital, and 18.5 percent in the nonprofit private hospital.

The perceived reasons for missed time (see Table 4.5) represent a wide range of factors that may or may not be under the control of the hospital director or even the central government secretary; but other factors clearly could be addressed through policy. In the opinion of both doctors and nurses, more than 40 percent of doctor absenteeism is attributed to lack of controls and multiple jobholding (i.e., simultaneous employment in several institutions). As multiple jobholding only generates absenteeism if there are no efficient controls (which is also true for other cited reasons for absenteeism), one can conclude that the lack of control is the principal determinant

Table 4.5 Medical Staff Perceptions of Doctor Absenteeism by Hospital and Cause (In percent)

Respondents:	Hospital								All	
	Auton.		Private		CGBA1		CGBA2			
Doctors or nurses	D	N	D	N	D	N	D	N	D	N
Causes:										
Low wages	1.7	5.6	3.8	8.2	13.3	19.2	13.7	9.1	8.0	10.5
Long shifts	8.6	11.1	0.0	4.1	4.7	7.7	4.8	8.5	4.6	7.9
Multiple jobholding	19.0	16.7	23.1	12.2	29.3	25.0	25.6	9.1	24.0	15.8
No controls	15.5	20.4	3.8	4.1	26.0	17.3	28.6	55.6	18.5	24.4
Lack of incentives	3.4	3.7	0.0	0.0	3.3	1.9	11.3	7.8	4.6	3.4
Stress	13.8	13.0	0.0	0.0	4.0	0.0	1.8	0.0	5.1	3.4
Illness	20.7	18.5	36.5	32.6	12.0	19.2	10.7	5.9	19.9	18.9
Studies/Congresses	6.9	3.7	17.3	14.3	6.0	1.9	3.6	3.9	8.3	5.8
Others	10.3	7.4	15.4	24.5	1.3	7.7	0.0	0.0	6.8	9.7

Notes: The question was: "Why do you think there is absenteeism among doctors in your hospital? Because of: (1) low wages, (2) excessively long shifts, (3) excessive multiple jobholding, (4) no controls, (5) no incentives to respect working hours, (6) others." As this was an open question, respondents could spontaneously add other reasons. For each hospital and each category, the results reported relate to the percentage of respondents who selected each cause as a proportion of respondents who suggested any cause. Column sums may not add up to 100 due to rounding.

in the opinion of these agents. By contrast, lack of controls seems to be a significantly weaker determinant of absenteeism in the nonprofit private hospital.

The lower level of missed days relative to missed work-shift hours is also consistent with respondent opinion that lax controls encourage absenteeism. Total absences are easier to control than hourly absenteeism because it is easier to record whether or not a particular staff member showed up for work on a particular day than to measure how many hours that person actually worked.

The fact that there is less day absenteeism than hourly absenteeism is also consistent with the absence of an effective incentive scheme. The existing attendance bonus system was introduced to reduce unjustified absenteeism, and is granted monthly to hospital staff members who record a maximum of one unjustified absence per month. Justified absences (e.g., illness, or the birth or death of a family member) do not affect the bonus, and the work attendance bonus can represent up to 15 percent of an agent's wage. But since attendance is measured only by whether or not the staff member showed up for work, staff can still receive the bonus while being absent during any given workday after "signing in." In direct interviews, upper management frequently emphasized the need for incentives to reduce absenteeism (Mera et al., 1999). Yet surveyed hospital staff thought lack of incentives was less important than hospital authorities suggested.

Using Public Resources to Benefit Private Practices

Other survey questions targeted perceptions of corruption from using public facilities and inputs for private benefit, diverting patients to private practice, and billing patients improperly. Most doctors (63.6 percent) stated that they *never* used hospital facilities to see private patients. But the figure differed across the sample hospitals. The nonprofit private hospital reported the highest share of replies that this practice exists (55.6 percent), while the CGBA hospitals reported shares of 22.2 percent and 39.3 percent, respectively. The share from the Autonomous Hospital was 28.6 percent, in between the rates at the two CGBA hospitals. Among doctors who acknowledged that they used public facilities for their private patients, a relatively small share — only 15.8 — believed it was for the physician's benefit. Instead, the most common explanations given by doctors for this misuse of public facilities were to guarantee continuity of treatment, for the convenience of patients, or because patients are too poor to afford treatment in a private facility.

Doctors reported that, on average, 11 percent of hospital patients are referred from the public facility to private practices (see Table 4.6). Very few physicians (less than 4 percent) think this referral rate exceeds 25 percent of patients. Surveyed nurses think that diversion of patients to private practice is more common than reported by doctors, but even so, about half of the nurses reported there was no diversion of hospital patients to private practice.

When patients were asked if "the doctors in this hospital suggest to their patients that they change to their private practice," only an average of 6.3 percent agreed (6.6 percent in the autonomous hospital, 3.4 percent in the nonprofit private hospital, 3.3 percent in CGBA1, and 10.7 percent in CGBA2).

Table 4.6 Incidence of Referring Hospital Patients to Private Practices and Its Causes

	Hospital				All
	Auton.	Private	CGBA1	CGBA2	
Share of patients (%) referred to private practice according to:					
Doctors	7.5	14.0	10.4	12.1	11.0
Nurses	7.9	30.0	17.4	25.0	19.2
Share of doctors (%) who say such referrals occur and attribute it to:					
Patient's request	22.2	37.5	35.0	38.5	35.0
Reducing waiting time	22.2	33.3	10.0	7.7	17.9
Improving treatment	22.2	4.2	35.0	19.2	19.1
The doctor's benefit	33.3	25.0	20.0	11.5	20.7
Others	0.0	0.0	0.0	23.1	7.3

Notes: For the first panel, the question was: "How often do you think the professionals in your hospital refer patients to their private practices? (1) All patients, (2) three of every four patients, (3) two of every four patients, (4) one of every four patients, (5) none." The percentage reported is based on the average responses of the interviewees. The second panel represents the response to a follow-up question for doctors who agreed that patients were being referred to private practice. They were asked: "What in your understanding is the origin of this practice? (1) Patient's request; (2) to reduce waiting time; (3) better-quality treatment; (4) for the doctor's benefit; (5) others."

Doctors gave various reasons for these referrals (Table 4.6). The principal explanation (cited by 34.9 percent of respondent physicians) is that patients themselves request the referral. Benefit to the physician is next in importance, cited by about one in five doctors; although reduced waiting time and better treatment are cited nearly as often. The one institutional exception to the high shares citing doctors' self-interest was CGBA2, where only 11 percent of respondents explained referrals this way, from a half to a third of the rates at the other hospitals.

Both doctors and nurses (but not patients) believe that the private hospital has the highest rate of diverting patients to private practice and the highest use of hospital facilities for treating private patients. Because of the variety of financial arrangements between the nonprofit facility and its physicians, it is difficult to determine if the observed referrals are an abusive practice or a normal form of medical attention in the private sector.

Perceptions of Theft and Bribery

The nursing staff was asked what share of supplies are stolen. The average estimated loss from theft was not large, about 2.7 percent. The highest levels (2.9 percent and 5.5 percent) were reported in the CGBA hospitals, about twice the rate in the autonomous hospital (1.9 percent) and eight times the rate in the nonprofit private hospital (only 0.5 percent).

An overwhelming convergence of opinion agreed that doctors did not request extra payments from patients. More than 90 percent of the nursing staff and 80 percent of patients concurred. And when extra payments were requested, they related to bonuses paid by the "hospital cooperative"[8] or payments for medical supplies. No patient or nurse in any of the four sample hospitals stated that patients were asked for improper payments. Nevertheless, 6.3 percent of patients did agree that "you have to pay a gratuity to the person in charge to avoid the queue." This share was less than 4 percent in all hospitals except CGBA1, where it was over 13 percent.

Hospital Corruption in Perspective

Lastly, doctors and nurses were asked to judge the level of public hospital corruption in a range of activities (see Table 4.7). Some implicitly would fall under their control, and others would be carried out by administrative authorities. In general the respondents perceived higher levels of corruption in activities controlled by authorities (contracting, purchases, and staff appointments) than in activities in which doctors and nurses participate directly.

Summary of Survey Findings

Of the different kinds of illegal activity considered in the survey, absenteeism seems to be the most serious form of abuse carried out by doctors and

---

[8] *Editor's note*: This refers to payments made by small, informal nongovernmental organizations, "*cooperadoras*," that are established to raise additional funds for schools or hospitals. Contributions to the public hospital cooperatives are supposed to be voluntary, but sometimes there is strong social pressure to contribute. There have been accusations concerning corruption in some of these organizations.

Table 4.7 Perceived Incidence of Public Hospital Corruption by Activity

Activity	Average (0 to 5)	Category
Bidding process for meals service	3.3	Moderate to high
Bidding process for cleaning services	3.2	Moderate to high
Bidding process for private security services	3.1	Moderate to high
Bidding process for input purchases	3.1	Moderate to high
Staff appointments	2.3	Low to moderate
Appropriation of inputs	1.9	Very low to low
Scheduling surgery dates	1.7	Very low to low
Diversion of patients to private practice	1.3	Very low to low

Note: Only doctors and nurses were asked this question: "In your understanding, is the level of corruption in the following activities in public hospitals: very high, high, moderate, low, very low, or nonexistent?" The responses were then ranked from 5 ("very high") to 0 ("nonexistent"), and simple averages were calculated.

nurses in their public duties. Medical staff pointed to a lack of adequate monitoring and controls as the primary cause. Administrative authorities, on the other hand, blamed the lack of material incentives. The evidence suggests that lack of controls and a lack of incentives (including a system that targets missed days, not missed hours) combine as major factors behind high rates of absenteeism. The survey also demonstrated that medical staff and patients think that referral of public hospital clients to private practice is not particularly serious and takes place largely for the benefit, or even at the request, of service users themselves. Charging patients improperly seems to be almost nonexistent, and supply theft also appears to be fairly limited.

Monitoring the Prices Hospitals Pay for Supplies

Another activity with high potential for corruption — through kickbacks, graft, or over-invoicing — is supply purchasing. There is some scope for such abuses to occur within CGBA hospitals because supply purchasing is highly decentralized. Each hospital has its own purchasing office for supplies, headed by its own manager. Because hospitals finance their supplies from the annual budget assigned to them by the Health Secretariat, decentralized purchasing should be an incentive to generate savings since unspent funds are retained by the hospital. They should also be interested in efficient purchasing with the funds they receive from billing services to Social Security Institutions (*Obras Sociales*). However, these incentives are constrained because the savings can only be used to buy more or better-quality supplies, and any unused funds must be returned to the CGBA at the end of the year.

On September 9, 1996, the CGBA Health Secretariat, through the Subsecretariat of Strategic Management, ordered the 33 institutions in its jurisdiction to supply detailed information for each purchase of a range of supplies, including date, price paid, quantity required, brand, supplier, modality used, and other supplementary information. Beginning October 7, 1996, the information supplied by each hospital was compiled and regularly sent back to all the hospitals, allowing administrators and managers to compare the prices they paid with those paid by other purchasers in the CGBA system. The format highlighted the highest and lowest prices for each input (CGBA, 1997a), including needles, syringes, intravenous solutions, antiseptics, medicinal gases, sanitary material, adhesive tape, x-ray film, and canalization material. No medicines were included. The price monitoring system generated data for purchases made between August 1996 and December 1997. The policy was halted in January 1998 when the CGBA implemented additional controls on purchases and contracting through a "Single Account System," ending the flow of data.

From the many supplies monitored by the Secretariat, this chapter studies 15, focusing on those that had the largest number of transactions within a particular category. All of the chosen supplies have a high degree of homogeneity so that any price differences cannot be attributed to differences in quality or usage. The selected products are:

- dextrose (5%, 500 ml)

- liquid oxygen

- physiological solution (500 ml)

- x-ray film (35 cm x 35 cm)

- ethyl alcohol (96%)

- sanitary adhesive tape (5 cm x 9 m)

- double-distilled water (500 ml)

- ◆ syringes (10 cc)

- ◆ hydrophilic cotton (500 g)

- ◆ needles (25/8 caliber)

- ◆ soapy povidone iodine (5%)

- ◆ nitrous oxide

- ◆ tubular hydrofoil gauze

- ◆ oxygenated water (100 volumes)

- ◆ intravenous Teflon™ catheter (N°22 G)

Initial data for four of the products (physiological solution, ethyl alcohol, soapy povidone iodine, and oxygenated water) includes August 1996, before the monitoring policy was implemented. Data for the other products follow the policy implementation. Although the government started monitoring the most homogeneous products first, all monitored supplies possess a significant degree of homogeneity. Not all of the CGBA hospitals purchased all the 15 supplies in our sample during the period under review. The resulting sample of transactions for these goods consisted of 1,866 observations.

Initially, five observations were excluded because the quantity purchased was missing and the prices and quantities of all transactions for a particular item were needed to obtain its weighted average price. For some transactions, the prices reported were excessively high in relation to this average.[9] To keep anomalous extremes from skewing the results, 11 observations were excluded because their reported prices were over 3.5 times higher than the average price.[10] Thus our final sample consists of 1,850 observations. See Table 4.8 for a list of variables and sample statistics.

Depending on the purchase amount and the urgency of need, there are four purchasing procedures: public bidding, private bidding, direct contracting, and emergency purchases. They are discussed in turn according to

---

[9] Given the exaggerated value of some of these prices, we think they are more likely to be typing errors or errors in product definition or measurement unit than acute episodes of corruption.

[10] We took this "magic" number of 3.5 from Borenstein and Rose (1994).

Table 4.8 Sample Statistics for Purchase Prices (1996–1997)

Variable	Number of observations	Mean	Standard deviation	Minimum	Maximum
Price (normalized)	1,850	1.06	0.30	0.27	4.16
Quantity (normalized)	1,850	1.00	1.51	0.00	26.01
Emergency	1,634	0.28	0.45	0.00	1.00
Direct contracting	1,634	0.19	0.39	0.00	1.00
Own resources	1,634	0.19	0.40	0.00	1.00
Decree 69	1,634	0.33	0.47	0.00	1.00
Private bidding	1,634	0.00	0.07	0.00	1.00
Public bidding	1,634	0.00	0.06	0.00	1.00
Beds	33	270.85	341.08	0.00	1,598.00
Visits	33	140,020	109,658	0.00	345,988
Efficiency wage	33	371.09	340.27	−214.49	1,105.76
Years of service	33	16.55	8.45	3.00	35.00
Years of education	33	12.92	2.35	7.00	17.00
Technology	33	2.01	0.84	1.00	4.00
Nominal wage	33	1,295.46	402.41	750.00	2,250.00
Woman	33	0.88	0.33	0.00	1.00
Head of family	33	0.67	0.48	0.00	1.00
Married	33	0.42	0.50	0.00	1.00
Partner	33	0.06	0.24	0.00	1.00
Divorced	33	0.27	0.45	0.00	1.00
Widow(er)	33	0.06	0.24	0.00	1.00
Complete primary	33	0.03	0.17	0.00	1.00
Incomplete secondary	33	0.09	0.29	0.00	1.00
Complete secondary	33	0.42	0.50	0.00	1.00
Incomplete tertiary	33	0.09	0.29	0.00	1.00
Complete tertiary	33	0.15	0.36	0.00	1.00
Incomplete university	33	0.06	0.24	0.00	1.00
Complete university	33	0.15	0.36	0.00	1.00
Experience	33	23.79	9.79	9.00	46.00

Note: See text for explanation of sample.

the strictness of the requirements for controlling transparency, with the most restrictive first.[11] In the period under study, payments to suppliers could either be made by the CGBA Health Secretariat or directly by the hospitals. Hospitals making payments either used funds earmarked for supplies under the now defunct Decree 69, or their own resources. Decree 69 funds were limited to public and private bidding processes or direct contracting; however information about which of these three alternatives was used for a specific transaction was not available. Similarly, information is unavailable about which procedure a hospital used in spending its own resources, even though these funds were generally used for emergency purchases. Consequently the transactions data were classified by modality into six categories: public bidding, private building, direct contracting, emergency purchases, Decree 69, and a hospital's own funds. Even so, the purchase modality is only known for 1,634 of the 1,850 observations, further reducing the sample size.

Initial analysis of the data shows a significant dispersion in the prices at which hospitals purchase their supplies. Table 4.9 shows sample statistics for the 15 selected products. It also shows two different measurements of price dispersion: the coefficient of variation and the ratio of maximum to minimum price (max-min ratio). Both measures demonstrate a high degree of dispersion. Averaging across all 15 supplies yields a coefficient of variation of 0.28 and a max-min ratio of 4.80.

It is apparent that there is no single "market price" at which hospitals buy these supplies, but rather a range of prices. Nor do we have a simple situation in which prices paid differ between hospitals but stay the same for any particular hospital. Breaking down an item's price variation between hospitals (interhospital variance) and the variation between different purchases of that item by the same hospital (intrahospital variance), we find that both are significant. The average interhospital coefficient of variation is 0.24, and the average intrahospital coefficient of variation is 0.16.[12] Not only

---

[11] The requirements for each purchase procedure differ with respect to minimum number of days, advance notice, and media used (official bulletin, hospital notice board, etc.) for publication of the invitation to bid, the minimum number of invitations sent to suppliers, the minimum number of bids requested, and the minimum number of days and media used for the publication of the pre-award (Mera et al., 1999).

[12] The coefficient of interhospital variation is calculated as the ratio of the interhospital standard deviation between hospitals and the average price, and the coefficient of intrahospital variation is calculated as the ratio of the standard deviation within hospitals and the average price.

Table 4.9 Price Dispersion Among CGBA Hospitals (1996–1997)

Product	Prices			Ratio	Standard deviation		Coefficient of variation		Number of:	
	Average	Maximum	Minimum	Max-Min			Between	Within	Hospitals	Observations
	(a)	(d)	(e)	(f) = (d)/(e)	(b)	(c) = (b)/(a)	hospitals	hospitals		
Double-distilled water	0.79	1.48	0.45	3.29	0.14	0.18	0.16	0.14	17	68
Oxygenated water	2.58	6.80	0.99	6.87	1.41	0.55	0.41	0.33	19	30
Disposable needles	0.29	0.10	0.01	9.50	0.01	0.04	0.03	0.03	27	146
Ethyl alcohol	1.22	4.64	0.46	10.09	0.38	0.31	0.20	0.25	31	158
Absorbent cotton	1.91	4.18	1.46	2.86	0.46	0.24	0.16	0.19	27	142
Catheter	0.87	1.90	0.57	3.33	0.33	0.38	0.34	0.20	20	52
Dextrose	0.81	1.98	0.50	3.96	0.15	0.19	0.27	0.11	28	251
Tubular gas	10.35	21.97	7.10	3.09	3.08	0.30	0.33	0.14	26	140
Povidone iodine	2.24	5.50	0.91	6.04	0.65	0.29	0.25	0.21	27	101
Syringe	0.11	0.32	0.06	5.52	0.04	0.35	0.27	0.18	31	155
Nitrous oxide	13.44	23.00	3.50	6.57	5.54	0.41	0.40	0.13	19	55
Liquid oxygen	2.01	3.50	1.15	3.04	0.44	0.22	0.20	0.09	21	146
X-ray film	0.93	1.40	0.79	1.77	0.12	0.13	0.08	0.11	22	98
Physiological solution	0.78	1.47	0.50	2.94	0.13	0.16	0.06	0.14	29	236
Adhesive tape	1.84	3.27	1.02	3.22	0.73	0.40	0.41	0.15	23	72
Average				**4.80**		**0.28**	**0.24**	**0.16**		

Note: Average, maximum and minimum prices are in U.S. dollars.

do different hospitals purchase the same item at different prices, but the same hospital also pays different prices for that item at different times. Surprisingly, for 4 of the 15 products, the intrahospital variation is greater than the interhospital variation.

Accounting for Large Price Variations

To better understand the dispersion of prices and use it to identify and measure graft, we can analyze the influence of a series of factors on the purchase prices of hospital supplies. Using each transaction as an observation, we can control for a series of variables:

$$\overline{P}_{ijh} = \alpha + \Phi X_i + \Theta X_{ijh} + \varepsilon_{ijh} \qquad [4.1]$$

where $\overline{P}_{ijh}$ is the price (normalized by the weighted average price) paid by hospital i for product j in purchase h obtained as:

$$\overline{P}_{ijh} = \frac{p_{ijh}}{\left(\dfrac{\sum_i \sum_h p_{ijh} q_{ijh}}{\sum_i \sum_h q_{ijh}} \right)} \qquad [4.2]$$

where p_{ijh} is the price paid by hospital i for product j in purchase h, q_{ijh} is the amount acquired by hospital i of product j in purchase h, X_i represents control variables related to hospital i, and X_{ijh} represents control variables related to the purchase of product j by hospital i in purchase h.

One of the first possible explanations for price dispersion is purchase volume. Hospitals that buy supplies in larger lots may obtain bulk discounts, while larger hospitals may enjoy the market power to negotiate lower prices. To address these factors, the control variables included hospital size, proxied by the number of beds and outpatient visits for each hospital,[13] and the size of each purchase, defined as the normalized average purchase quantity of

---

[13] The number of beds relates to average availability in 1997. The number of outpatient visits relates to the total for the second half of 1997. The number of hospital discharges in the second half of 1997 was also used, with no significant change in results. There is a high correlation among these three measures of hospital size.

each item. Since these relationships are unlikely to be linear, the square of the size variables was also included.

The results presented in Table 4.10 confirm that larger hospitals do, indeed, obtain lower prices. This result holds in the first regression (see column 1 in Table 4.10) when hospital size is measured by the number of beds. In the other four regressions, the coefficient is positive because of the inclusion of the squared term (whose coefficient is negative) and other control factors like the number of visits. When hospital size is measured by the number of visits, the effect is consistently strong and associated with lower purchase prices. The normalized quantity is also consistently significant and negative across all five regressions, suggesting that in practice there are discounts for quantity.[14]

Going beyond these control factors, one needs to investigate the impact of different procurement procedures on prices. CGBA hospitals use different procedures for controlling purchase transparency, depending on the volume and degree of urgency. The effect of these administrative controls on prices is measured with dummy variables for each of the six modalities described above. The regression equation is therefore augmented as:

$$\bar{P}_{ijh} = \Phi X_i + \Theta X_{ijh} + \Omega M_{ijh} + \varepsilon_{ijh} \qquad [4.3]$$

where M_{ijh} is the modality used by hospital i in the purchase h of product j.

The results are presented in column 2 of Table 4.10.[15]

We then classified these six modalities into two categories — those with stronger and those with weaker controls, using two alternative groupings. Specifically, we estimated:

$$\bar{P}_{ijh} = \alpha + \Phi X_i + \Theta X_{ijh} + \beta C_{ijh} + \varepsilon_{ijh} \qquad [4.4]$$

where $C1_{ijh}$ is the high control dummy variable valued at 1 when M_{ijh} is either public bidding, private bidding, direct contracting, or Decree 69,

---

[14] When the total quantity purchased by a given hospital of each item over the entire period under consideration is included as a control variable, the results are also robust.

[15] The number of observations falls to 1,634 because of the lack of information on the purchase modality in the other observations.

Table 4.10 Determinants of Normalized Purchase Prices

Variables	1	2	3	4	5
Beds (x 10^{-4})	**-5.30**	**3.06**	**2.75**	**2.81**	**2.87**
	-2.18	-2.22	-2.00	-2.04	-2.07
Visits (x 10^{-7})		**-8.01**	**-7.85**	**-8.63**	**-7.95**
		-2.11	-2.10	-2.34	-2.09
Beds² (x 10^{-7})		**-2.38**	**-2.15**	**-2.19**	**2.23**
		-2.67	-2.45	-2.49	-2.53
Visits² (x 10^{-13})		-8.61	7.80	9.90	9.34
		-0.91	-0.82	-1.06	-0.98
Normalized quantity	**-0.03**	**-0.04**	**-0.04**	**-0.04**	**-0.04**
(NQ)	-6.24	-5.34	-5.48	-5.79	-5.37
NQ² (x 10^{-3})		**1.63**	**1.64**	**1.59**	**1.66**
		-2.85	-2.85	-2.92	-2.87
Own resources		**1.17**			
		-34.67			
Decree 69		**1.13**			
		-29.01			
Public bidding		**1.10**			
		-15.69			
Private bidding		**1.29**			
		-11.24			
Direct contracting		**1.16**			
		-29.58			
Emergency		**1.14**			
		-29.07			
Strong controls 1			-0.01		
			-0.65		
Strong controls 2				-0.027*	
				-1.66	
Purchase modalities					Yes
Monthly effects					Yes
F-statistic					**8.42**
Observations	1,850	1,634	1,634	1,634	1,634
R²	0.021	0.041	0.037	0.038	0.053

Notes: Robust t-statistics are in italics. Boldface indicates statistically significant at the 5% level. The asterisk (*) indicates statistically significant at the 10% level. Null hypothesis for the F-statistic is that the monthly effects are jointly zero.

and at 0 when M_{ijh} is a hospital's own resources or an emergency purchase; and $C2_{ijh}$ is the high control dummy variable valued at 1 when M_{ijh} is either public bidding, private bidding, or Decree 69, and valued at 0 when M_{ijh} is direct contracting, a hospital's own resources, or an emergency purchase.

The results shown in columns 3 and 4 of Table 4.10 suggest, as might be expected, that hospitals pay lower prices when they use procedures that involve a greater degree of control. However the results in column 3 show that this finding is not robust to changes in our definitions.

An Evaluation of the Price Monitoring Policy

To facilitate interpretation of the statistical analysis, it is worthwhile to consider the history and dynamics of the price monitoring policy. As stated earlier, the price monitoring policy began in September 1996 when the CGBA Health Secretariat required the 33 institutions under its authority to send information to it on their monthly purchases of a specific set of supplies. Starting in October 1996, the compiled information from all the hospitals began to be sent regularly to each hospital.

Three hypotheses can be used to explain the effects of policy implementation on subsequent purchase prices. First, if overpricing is due to corruption and monitoring can identify the hospitals that pay higher prices, the fear of future audits and reprimands should have induced an immediate fall in prices as soon as the Secretariat began to request the information. Although price comparisons were not in fact part of a system of bonuses and punishment, purchase managers did not know at the time how the Secretariat would use the information. Second, price variation might be due to inefficiency. If the price differential is due to inadequate efforts by purchase managers and the monitoring can identify those who are inefficient, the fear of reprimands might reduce the prices as soon as the Secretariat began requesting the information. Third, the price differentials could be a consequence of asymmetries in information. If some hospitals paid more because they were unaware of the existence of cheaper suppliers or because they did not know that a particular supplier was charging discriminatory prices, the monitoring policy would begin to fill that vacuum and steer managers toward lower-cost sources. Obviously all three effects could also be operating at the same time.

Figure 4.1 Estimated Monthly Effects

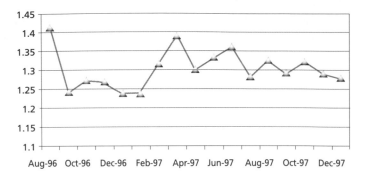

Note: The effects are detailed in Schargrodsky et al. (2000,Table XIII).

To evaluate the effect of the monitoring policy, we calculated the regression of the normalized prices against our control variables, adding a fixed monthly effect:

$$\bar{P}_{ijh} = \Phi X_i + \Theta X_{ijh} + \Omega M_{ijh} + \Psi T_t + \varepsilon_{ijh} \qquad [4.5]$$

where T_t is the fixed monthly effect (t).

The results of the regression, given in column 5 of Table 4.10, show that the fixed monthly coefficients are statistically significant. The estimated monthly coefficients are presented in Figure 4.1.

The monthly effect of the policy was for prices to fall immediately in September 1996 and to stay down, until bottoming out in December 1996. After controlling for purchase volumes and hospital size, prices fell an average of 12 percent in September 1996, and were 13 percent below their initial level in December 1996.[16] Beginning in January 1997 the price levels increased, although they never reached the level of August 1996.[17] If the initial fall in prices was generated by the policy of transparency implemented by the Secretariat, the transitory effect seems to have been greater than the permanent effect.

---

[16] For more details of this statistical analysis see Schargrodsky et al. (2000). Di Tella (1997) also found an immediate negative effect of the Secretariat monitoring policy on prices.

[17] The F statistic for the null hypothesis of equal monthly coefficients is 2.55 (significant to 7.3 percent) for August 1996 against December 1997.

The trend in price variations supports the idea that the policy's transitory effect was greater than its permanent effect. Figure 4.2 shows the trend of the coefficient of variation (averaged across goods) during the period under consideration.

Although other factors may affect these purchase prices, the evidence suggests that the policy of transparency had a strong initial effect, and that its effectiveness later declined. The large immediate fall in prices reduces support for the idea that the monitoring policy affected prices only through resolving information asymmetries. The fact that the prices began to fall in September, when the price information was requested, and not in October, when the price comparisons began to be disseminated, suggests that the initial effect can be explained only by the corruption or efficiency hypotheses.

Although this particular evidence does not allow us to distinguish the corruption hypothesis from the inefficiency hypothesis, additional anecdotal evidence does indeed support the corruption hypothesis. The CGBA Health Secretariat implemented the monitoring policy because it believed there was corruption in hospital supply purchases. The possibility of corruption in procurement is also suggested by some cases in which CGBA hospital staff members under suspicion of corruption were transferred to other posts. The survey of doctors and nurses demonstrated substantial agreement with this supposition. Although their survey responses did not single out pro-

Figure 4.2 Coefficient of Variation for Purchase Prices

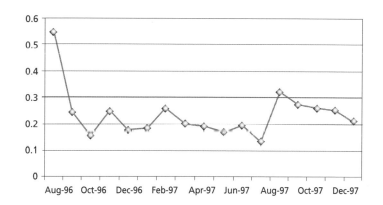

Note: The price dispersion measure is detailed in Schargrodsky et al. (2000, Table XIII).

curement as the most corrupt activity in public hospitals, the level was still thought to be between moderate and high.

The best explanation for the pattern of prices and price dispersion is corruption in procurement. By announcing that it would publish the procurement prices, the CGBA Health Secretariat increased the chance of detection and punishment for corrupt supply purchases. This concern continued through December 1996, at which time it became apparent that the information being compiled was not going to be used to determine bonuses or mete out punishment. Prices, and price dispersion, subsequently increased.

Corruption and Efficiency Wages

If corruption in hospital supply purchasing exists, is it possible to identify what factors encourage or discourage such behavior? One potential factor is the wage level, and particularly how much an individual is paid over what he or she could earn in another job. Economists have identified this kind of wage premium as an inducement for workers to be more productive since another job at similar pay will not be available if they are dismissed. Such a wage premium is called the "efficiency wage," and higher efficiency wages are expected to induce workers to perform more efficiently (Yellen, 1984; Shapiro and Stiglitz, 1984). In the case of CGBA, hospitals with purchase managers receiving higher efficiency wages should be paying less for hospital supplies.

To estimate the efficiency wages of the purchase managers, all 33 were asked about their nominal wage, gender, education level, age, length of service, status as head of household, and marital status. The efficiency wage was then calculated as the difference between the reported wage and the estimated wage that these agents would obtain in the labor market based on their personal characteristics.

The first step was to calculate the impact of personal characteristics on earnings in the labor market. This is done with a standard Mincerian wage equation, separately for men and women.[18] The expected market wage for any particular purchasing manager is calculated as:

---

[18] We thank Sebastián Galiani for his cooperation with the data from the INDEC Permanent Household Survey used to estimate this equation. The specific estimates for these wage equations can be found in Schargrodsky et al. (2000, Appendix II).

$$\hat{W}_i = \hat{B}C_i \qquad\qquad [4.6]$$

where $\hat{W}_i$ is the expected market wage for hospital purchase manager i, C_i represents the hospital purchase manager's personal characteristics (experience, education level, length of service, head of household or not, and marital status), and $\hat{B}$ represents the coefficients of the Mincerian wage equation.

The efficiency wage for each manager is then calculated simply by subtracting the expected market wage from the reported wage, or:

$$EW_i = W_i - \hat{W}_i \qquad\qquad [4.7]$$

where EW_i is the estimated efficiency wage of hospital purchase manager (i), and W_i is the nominal wage of hospital purchase manager i.

In the survey, CGBA hospital purchase managers reported average monthly salaries of US$1,295.[19] Based on calculations using the equations above, that average is US$375 above expected earnings in the labor market, which means they receive a bonus of 28 percent over what they could earn elsewhere. In fact, this overestimates the market wage of these agents and, therefore, underestimates the efficiency wage because it implicitly assumes that a purchase manager would immediately obtain another job after being dismissed from the public sector. This would have been unlikely given the high rate of unemployment in Argentina at the time price monitoring was taking place. The standard deviation of this efficiency wage — US$340 — is also significant.

Based on these calculations, a two-stage procedure was used to analyze the hypothesis that the efficiency wage of each hospital's purchase manager would affect the prices the hospitals pay for supplies. First, an indicator was obtained that measures the average prices paid by each hospital in all of its transactions, net of the effect of control variables. To do this, dummy variables (fixed effects for each hospital) were introduced into the regression that analyzes the determinants of purchase prices:

$$P_{ijh} = \Gamma F_i + \Theta X_{ijht} + \Omega M_{ijht} + \Psi T_t + \varepsilon_{ijh} \qquad\qquad [4.8]$$

where F_i is the fixed effect of hospital i.

---

[19] The foreign exchange rate in Argentina is fixed at $Arg1 = US$1.

After controlling for all the other variables, statistically significant systematic differences in the prices paid by hospitals for their supplies still exist. And these differences are large. The lowest prices paid by a hospital are 68 percent of the estimated prices paid by the highest.[20]

Now it is possible, after controlling for other factors, to see if purchase managers' wages affect the prices paid by their hospitals. This is done through a regression in which the hospital fixed effects (the average difference in purchase prices) estimated in the first stage become the dependent variable in a new regression. The efficiency wages and other control variables are included as explanatory variables. Specifically:

$$\hat{\Gamma}_i = \alpha_0 + \alpha_1 EW_i + \alpha_2 Z_i + \varepsilon_i \qquad [4.9]$$

where $\hat{\Gamma}_i$ represents the estimated fixed effects of hospital i, and Z_i represents the control factors in hospital i.

The results, presented in Table 4.11, show a negative but statistically insignificant relationship between efficiency wages and input purchase prices. This result is robust to the use of different controls: hospital size (number of visits), purchase manager's years of education, purchase manager's years of service in the CGBA hospital system, and the technological level of the purchasing office (staff/computers ratio). The results are also robust using the number of beds as an indicator of size, and length of time in the position of purchase manager as the length-of-service variable (not shown). The regressions confirm that larger hospitals pay lower prices. The rest of the controls are not significant.

What does the absence of an association between efficiency wages and our corruption index mean? One possible explanation of the finding is that there are no corrupt practices in the purchase of hospital inputs. However this is not consistent with the evidence on purchase prices above or the opinions of medical personnel and the Health Secretariat. A second argument is that the theory is mistaken because agents do not take into account material incentives when they decide how to behave. The widespread use of incentive systems in the private sector refutes this interpretation. Another explanation is that purchase managers do not influence contracting in CGBA hospitals, but simply implement the decisions of other agents (hospital directors,

---

[20] For more details on this regression, see Schargrodsky et al. (2000, Table XIV).

Table 4.11 The Impact of Wages on the Hospital Procurement Corruption Index

Variables	1	2	3	4	5	6
Efficiency wage	−0.48	−1.16	−1.63	−0.37	−1.18	−1.26
(x 10^{-5})	*−0.11*	*−0.26*	*−0.33*	*−0.08*	*−0.25*	*−0.25*
Visits (x 10^{-7})		**−4.21**	**−4.10**	−3.55	**−4.21**	−3.05
	−2.42	*−2.33*	*−2.08*	*−2.35*	*−1.63*	
Schooling			−0.31			−0.82
(years x 10^{-2})			*−0.31*			*−0.76*
Experience				−0.27		−0.36
(years x 10^{-2})				*−1.11*		*−1.16*
Technology					3.35	−11.34
(pers/comp x 10^{-4})					*−0.01*	*−0.04*
Observations	33	33	33	33	33	33
R^2	0.0002	0.146	0.150	0.179	0.146	0.200

Notes: Robust t-statistics are in italics. Boldface indicates statistically significant at the 5% level. The dependent variable is the hospital fixed effects as estimated in equation 4.8 and reported in Schargrodsky et al. (2000).

for example). This is not the opinion of surveyed purchase managers themselves. In that survey, 28 out of 33 purchase managers reported that they have moderate, strong, or very strong influence over the procurement process.

The most likely explanation is that efficiency wages do not stop corrupt practices because the agents do not perceive that punishment is probable. In fact, no CGBA hospital purchase manager has ever been investigated or removed from his job as a result of information obtained through the monitoring policy. If the agents believe there is no risk of losing their jobs when they behave improperly, the payment of efficiency wages can do little to end corrupt practices. Even if only a share of purchase managers consider the probability of losing their jobs to be null, the econometric results will show, as they do, a statistically insignificant relationship between efficiency wages and the purchase prices of inputs.

Conclusions

This chapter began with the results of surveys of doctors, nurses, and patients. Of the various forms of improper practices that were considered, respondents saw absenteeism among doctors as their most serious abuse of public trust. In contrast, treatment of private patients in public hospital facilities, referral of patients to private practice, requests for improper payments from patients, and theft of supplies were not perceived to be major problems.

This led to consideration of two related questions using hard data from hospital procurement. First, did the CGBA Health Secretariat's new monitoring policy affect supply purchase prices? The results indicate that the policy reduced prices but that the transitory exceeded the permanent effect. The immediate fall in prices as soon as the Health Secretariat began to require information from hospitals, and before any price comparisons were made known, suggests that the monitoring policy's impact could not be explained by disseminating better information. Instead it appears that the monitoring policy induced purchase managers to reduce their involvement in corrupt practices or to work more efficiently.

Second, do wages of hospital purchase managers affect supply purchase prices? The empirical evidence does not support such a claim since there was no measurable impact of efficiency wages on purchase prices. It seems likely that the efficiency wages do not put an end to corrupt practices because the agents do not perceive a positive probability of punishment. If true, this implies that raising wages for purchasing managers in the public sector would by itself probably not have much effect on corruption. Apparently pay raises must be accompanied by monitoring and control policies so that agents will know there is some chance of losing their jobs if they behave inappropriately.

Implementation of a system of bonuses and punishments to reduce corruption in the public sector is not a simple task. However, evaluation of the Secretariat's monitoring policy generates some optimism about its possible effectiveness. As long as there was uncertainty about how the Secretariat would use the price information, the policy had a significant effect on prices. Only when the purchase managers saw that the price comparisons were not accompanied by other measures did the effect diminish.

CHAPTER 5

Induced Demand and Absenteeism in Peruvian Hospitals

Lorena Alcázar and Raúl Andrade

This chapter analyzes the relationship between institutional arrangements, incentives, and corruption in four Peruvian hospitals. It focuses on two particular types of corrupt practice: absenteeism by doctors and provision of unnecessary services (i.e., induced demand). One of the hospitals was operated in the private sector. Of the three public-sector hospitals, two were under the aegis of the Health Ministry (MINSA), and operated with different degrees of autonomy, and one was operated by the social security institute (ESSALUD). Absenteeism was analyzed using data from surveys of doctors and nurses. The survey analysis indicates that the different incentives faced by doctors, depending on their employment status, are significant factors in explaining high rates of absenteeism. Induced demand was analyzed with data on registered births at each of three hospitals to see whether unnecessary Cesarean sections were carried out. After controlling for medically relevant variables such as the mother's health, gestational age, and birthweight, the private-sector and social-security hospitals had significantly higher Cesarean rates. Furthermore the doctor's employment status and ability to schedule deliveries (whether or not delivery was on a weekend or holiday) were strongly associated with the likelihood of Cesarean delivery. Finally these analyses — and survey evidence on perceptions of corruption, transparency, mechanisms of control, and likelihood of punishment — are used to examine the implications for policies to reduce corruption and improve hospital performance.

Introduction

Since 1990, public opinion in Lima has ranked corruption as being between the third and sixth most important national problem.[1] However, there are very few studies and little information on the extent, characteristics, and impact of corruption in specific sectors. Attention instead has tended to focus on specific criminal investigations, while attempts to use a more systematic approach are rare. The health sector is no exception.

Analyzing how corruption is affected by institutional arrangements in hospitals is possible in Peru because health service provision by public hospitals is in the process of being changed. First, a new organizational model of resource allocation related to demand for services is being applied in some public hospitals operated by the Health Ministry (MINSA), while other public hospitals continue to receive allocations based on existing levels of infrastructure and personnel. These pilot experiments are being implemented under an annually negotiated management agreement called the Programa de Administración de Acuerdos de Gestión (PAAG). A second major change is taking place under Law 27056, which created a new social security system for health, the Seguro Social de Salud (ESSALUD), out of the separation of the pension and health insurance branches of the old social security system, the Instituto Peruano de Seguridad Social (IPSS). The social security hospitals are in a state of uncertainty because the implications of ESSALUD are still unknown. The Constitution of 1979 had recognized the IPSS as an "independent, decentralized institution" and gave it significant independence from the executive branch. The new law, however, attaches ESSALUD to the Ministry of Labor and Social Promotion. Although ESSALUD is still charged with providing full preventative, curative, and recuperative health services for industrial accidents and diseases in general, it will expand coverage to include unaffiliated and low-income groups under mandated programs whose characteristics and financing remain unspecified.

A third change affects both MINSA and ESSALUD hospitals, which are now expected to compete with new private health service entities, Entidades Prestadoras de Salud (EPSs). This larger health sector reform ini-

---

[1] Surveys conducted by Apoyo Opinión and Mercado S.A.

tiative increases the importance of studying and understanding how public hospitals function and respond to different forms of governance and incentives.

This chapter analyzes public hospital corruption from an institutional perspective. Specifically, it analyzes how organizational structure influences the type and degree of corruption, and recommends policies to combat the identified problems. Two types of corruption are addressed directly: (1) absenteeism, or payments to doctors even when they did not work, and (2) the provision of unnecessary medical services, i.e., medical treatments beyond what is considered to be "technically indicated" by a patient's condition.

Four Lima hospitals, characterized by markedly different institutional arrangements, cooperated in this study. The principal organizational differences among the hospitals stem from three different forms of ownership: (1) MINSA-operated public hospitals, (2) ESSALUD-operated public hospitals, and (3) private clinics. One hospital was chosen for each ownership category except MINSA, for which two hospitals were included — one using PAAG and one operating under traditional budgeting.

Evidence for this study was obtained from surveys and hospital records. First, doctors, nurses, and patients were surveyed in each hospital. Hospital officials were also interviewed to obtain their views of hospital management in general and of corruption, with particular emphasis on the problem of absenteeism. Second, the medical records of all mothers who gave birth in three of the four hospitals during 1998 were examined in order to analyze the relationship between the actual and technically indicated types of delivery.

Health Services in Peru

In Peru, both public and private entities deliver health care services. The public sector is comprised of the Health Ministry,[2] the Peruvian Institute of Social Security (now ESSALUD), the Health Department of the Armed

---

[2] The Health Ministry is the executive branch agency that governs the health sector and is responsible for regulating and supervising the implementation of national health policy.

and Police Forces, and the Beneficiencia (a charity organization). The private sector can be subdivided into two principal groups: for-profit clinics and private practices, and nonprofit providers such as NGOs, parishes, etc.

According to the latest MINSA census, following recent efforts to expand physical access to health services, the Ministry operates over 5,933 health establishments nationally. Among these are 136 hospitals, 28 of which are in metropolitan Lima. ESSALUD has 282 establishments, 71 of which are hospitals (17 in Lima). The private sector is comprised of 689 establishments, 202 of which are commercial hospitals (87 in Lima) and another 33 are nonprofit hospitals. Although most hospitals in Peru and in metropolitan Lima are in the private sector, public hospitals operated by MINSA account for the majority of admissions (see Figure 5.1).

In the public sector, ESSALUD is perceived to have more-modern and better-quality equipment and capital goods than MINSA. This contributes to the perception that ESSALUD doctors, through self-selection, are more qualified and professional than other public-sector doctors; that is, ESSALUD attracts doctors who seek access to more-modern technology and can pick

Figure 5.1 Shares of Hospitals and Hospitalizations by Ownership (In percent)

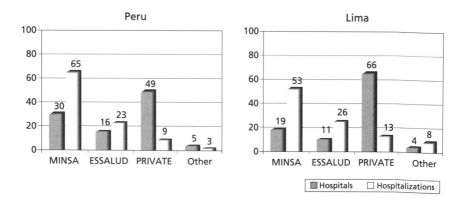

Source: II Census of Health Infrastructure and Resources in Health Sector. Ministry of Health, Office of Statistics and Informatics; World Bank, 1999.

the best applicants for employment. No specific evidence is available to evaluate this perception. However it is true that MINSA hospitals are generally older than ESSALUD hospitals. For example, 33 percent of MINSA hospitals have been operating for 10 to 25 years, compared with only 24 percent of ESSALUD hospitals.

The Ministry of Health clearly has more physical and human resources than either ESSALUD or the private sector (see Table 5.1). MINSA has almost twice as many hospitals as ESSALUD, and 50 percent more beds per hospital, with approximately the same occupation rate. MINSA also has more doctors per hospital, but productivity appears to be significantly higher in the ESSALUD facilities. Each doctor attends to an average of 2.7 patients per day in ESSALUD hospitals, compared to only 1.6 patients per day in MINSA hospitals. Interestingly, the average for the private sector is less than 1 patient per day.

Table 5.1 Health Sector Resources in Peru (1998)

	Public sector	MINSA	ESSALUD	Private sector
Physical resource indicators				
Hospitals	237	136	71	235
Beds per hospital	102.8	119.7	76.5	27
Unoccupied beds (%)	43.8	45.0	43.4	41.9
Human resource indicators				
Doctors	16,309	10,131	4,448	8,401
Doctors per hospital	68.8	74.5	62.6	41.6
Patients	11,376,016	5,106,930	3,704,075	1,039142
Consultations	23,963,934	10,192,776	8,833,468	1,760,818
Patients/doctor/day	2.23	1.61	2.66	0.39
Consultations/doctor/day	4.7	3.22	6.36	0.67

Source: II Census of Health Sector Infrastructure and Resources, Ministry of Health, Office of Statistics and Informatics.

Notes: "Private sector" includes all private facilities for "physical resource indicators," but only for-profit facilities for "human resource indicators." Additional data can be found in Alcázar and Andrade (2000, tables 1 and 2).

Institutional Differences Among Hospitals

The hospitals function under different institutional arrangements depending on the organization to which they belong. Private-sector hospitals are managed with unfettered autonomy and respond to incentives generated by the people who pay for their services. Within the public sector, the principal institutional difference is that MINSA hospitals are administered in a more decentralized fashion than are ESSALUD hospitals.

MINSA hospitals are organized according to Ministry regulations. The MINSA hospitals are managed by a director-general, an executive director, and an administrative director, all of whom are appointed by the Ministry. In practice, however, hospitals generally operate with only an executive director and a deputy director. These directors report directly to the Ministry, but are free to run day-to-day hospital administration with little interference. Serving under them are directors of training, welfare services, and research, followed by the heads of personnel, logistics, stores, and statistics, among others. Some hospitals have consultative councils of section directors to which the executive directors will submit certain kinds of decisions for review.

ESSALUD hospitals have a similar structure, but with "managers" instead of "directors." The hospital board is the highest authority in an ESSALUD hospital. It includes the hospital's general manager, although he or she never serves as board president. Since ESSALUD's executive management designates board members and each board reports to ESSALUD's presidency, the central office is more involved in hospital decision-making. The scope of action for ESSALUD hospitals is more regulated than MINSA's in terms of organization, administrative procedures, and resource management.

Budget Guidelines and Financing

MINSA hospital budgets are formulated according to the needs determined by each board, although the process is largely tied to guidelines set by previous years. By contrast, the budget of an ESSALUD hospital is defined by the central administrative office, based on targets it sets in consultation with hospital managers. In private clinics, budgets are defined by the institution's income and established needs. While the budgetary systems in the public sector depend more on political considerations than on the quality and quantity of services, the private sector's general reliance on fee for service generates incentives to prescribe more services, some of which are unnecessary (Wouters, 1998).

MINSA hospital budgets are funded from two principal sources: the public treasury and user charges. The former is used to pay wages and support departmental costs, while the latter covers most other expenses. Additionally some donations are received for purchasing specific infrastructure and equipment.

The resources to finance the ESSALUD budget come from payroll taxes (9 percent of wages) and from taxes levied on retirees (4 percent of pensions). Thus, ESSALUD hospitals have less budgetary independence than the MINSA hospitals, which are able to generate their own resources and execute their budget with little interference from the Ministry.

In the private sector, hospitals are financed from the fees they charge. According to interviews, pharmaceutical revenues produce most of the income. Other funds come from proportional fees paid by doctors for services provided in the facility (between 10 percent and 20 percent of the physician's fees), and from billing patients for hospital services.

Billing and Patient Care

Patients in MINSA hospitals also pay fees for services. However there is no centrally mandated policy that establishes a clear method for defining what those charges should be. In general, the fees are determined without considering technical criteria and with no exact knowledge of the hospital's cost structure or the demand for its services. Patients who cannot afford the fees can apply to the government social assistance office to see if they qualify for free services. However the process is very cumbersome, with a separate procedure required for each medical prescription or service, and the head of the social assistance office enjoys great discretion in determining eligibility, with no effective accountability mechanism.

In ESSALUD hospitals, incoming patients are guided by social workers through the admissions process. Patients covered by ESSALUD have, in effect, prepaid for services through their social security contributions, and so make no further payments to the hospital.

Private-sector clinics are paid on a fee-for-service basis. In general, their patients have private insurance plans that cover most of the expenses, based on rates negotiated between the insurance company and the clinic.

The patient is responsible for paying deductibles and any uncovered services. Patients who are not covered by their employer or by a private insurance plan, and who cannot afford to pay, may apply to social assistance programs. But generally, they receive free treatment only in emergencies, after which they are transferred to a MINSA hospital.

Transparent Decision-Making and Accountability

In MINSA hospitals, management often consults with an advisory committee on important decisions. However this system is not uniformly observed and some advisory committees have not met for years or sometimes only select committee members are consulted. Generally the decision-making process is not transparent. In addition, there are no effective communication channels between the medical staff and management. A high percentage of MINSA-affiliated doctors who participated in the study did not know about various management procedures in their hospitals.

In these hospitals, section chiefs evaluate the doctors in each section. Thus section chiefs have a great deal of discretionary authority. Evaluations are generally based on the number of patients a doctor sees per day, in line with the parameters recommended by the World Health Organization (WHO), although these are not defined for all specialties, depend on many other factors, and are generally not respected.

In the ESSALUD system, a control body (Inspectorate) visits each hospital, creating an incentive for more-transparent decision making. Oversight is also heightened because the hospital boards are appointed by the central office and are directly accountable to it. There is also a review council, or *consejo de vigilancia*, which approves projects above a certain size (such as public procurement). However communication channels between the medical staff and hospital management are seriously deficient, although the situation is slightly better than in the MINSA hospitals. With respect to personnel evaluation, ESSALUD has no central policy; each hospital may or may not evaluate its doctors, and each hospital uses its own criteria for these evaluations. Accountability is also enhanced by the presence of a centralized Process Improvement Office that receives complaints from patients regarding poor treatment or other irregularities.

In the private clinics, decisions are submitted by the medical director and the executive director to the board, which makes final decisions. Any medical partner may attend the meetings and participate in the decision. As in the other hospitals participating in the study, a large share of doctors were not aware of or were mistaken about the existence of administrative procedures.

Employment Contracts and Job Security

In the MINSA and ESSALUD hospitals, as in other public institutions, workers are hired under two main types of employment arrangement: by "appointment" (*nombrado*) or for a fixed-term (*contratado*). The laws governing these two forms are confusing, and each is governed by different specifications. There are, however, two principal differences between appointed and fixed-term employees. First, appointed employees enjoy job security, while fixed-term employees have renewable contracts (with terms ranging from three months to one year). Second, fixed-term staff members are not entitled to benefits enjoyed by appointed staff, such as vacations, bonuses, and other incentives (e.g., food baskets). The difference in job security, in particular, has important implications for doctors' performance. It is much easier to dismiss a fixed-term physician than one who is appointed.

Neither employment arrangement is predominant. In fact, there are almost as many fixed-term as appointed doctors in Peru, 12,288 and 12,420, respectively. However in metropolitan Lima, fixed-term doctors outnumber appointed doctors by about 10 percent, numbering 7,651 and 6,978, respectively.[3]

In addition to this difference in forms of employment, which exist in all public-sector facilities, MINSA and the ESSALUD hospitals also have different contracting systems. MINSA hospitals do their own hiring, subject only to the Ministry's pro forma approval. In ESSALUD, hiring is handled by a central human resources department, and is based on the central office's determination of each hospital's requirements.

Beyond these features, the MINSA and ESSALUD hospitals face staff problems that are common to most of the Peruvian public administration, namely low pay and a shortage of qualified personnel (Instituto APOYO, 1999).

---

[3] Ministry of Health, (1998).

Characteristics of Four Hospitals

To analyze the impact of these differing institutional arrangements on the extent of corruption in public hospitals, four hospitals with differing characteristics were selected for study. The first hospital, denoted MINSA1, is owned by the Ministry of Health and operates under the Ministry's traditional form of management. MINSA1 specializes in maternity care and pediatrics, and its executive director is assisted by eight administrative managers (accountants and legal advisers) and eight medical managers (doctors). The next level is comprised of assistant managers, followed by the departments involved in welfare and support activities. The medical managers receive training in administration and accounting, but the hospital still has a reputation for bad management involving administrative errors and irregularities. As a case in point, during the period of research, workers at MINSA1 went on a 24-hour strike. Although the strike was originally called to protest a decision not to pay the end-of-year bonus, it escalated into an accusation that the executive director misappropriated funds and a call for his dismissal. Specific charges aside, an impression was conveyed of general administrative disorder.

In this hospital, appointed personnel receive a monthly food basket valued at S/. 100 (US$30). Although this food basket represents 5 percent or less of a doctor's pay, doctors in various hospitals reported in interviews that it is still considered an important subsidy. The basket contains basic food items such as milk, rice, sugar, vegetables, pasta, etc.

The second hospital, denoted MINSA-2, is also operated by the Ministry of Health, but it is taking part in the pilot stage of PAAG. The highest authority is comprised of the executive managers. Beneath them are deputy managers and the operational sections, which are defined by PAAG rules as obstetrics and gynecology, surgery, general medicine, radiology, diagnostic support (pathology, physical rehabilitation), and pharmacy.

The appointed personnel in MINSA2 also receive a monthly food basket. In the future, distribution of this benefit will depend on an individual doctor's productivity — the first initiative of its kind in the public health sector.

The third hospital is operated by the Social Security Institute and will be denoted ESSALUD1. Unlike the MINSA hospitals, its executive management is supported by three medical and two administrative divisions. The next level consists of a number of departments and services. This hospital follows ESSALUD's centralized regulations that prohibit food baskets or other incentives.

The fourth hospital is a private clinic, denoted as Private1. Like many in its sector, Private1 is owned by medical partners, many of whom are unfamiliar with administration and management techniques. At the time of the study, Private1 was considering several changes to raise efficiency, such as redefining the functions of its executive director and the way it manages its financial accounts. The highest authority in the clinic is a board, comprised of the 11 medical partners, one of whom is elected executive president. The board appoints an executive director, who represents the board in the hospital. Hospital doctors are divided into three groups: the previously mentioned owners (11 medical partners), associates (who respond directly to a particular partner), and fixed-term doctors.

The four hospitals vary in size — from 101 beds in Private1 to nearly 1,500 in ESSALUD1 (see Table 5.2). More than 35 percent of the doctors at MINSA1 and MINSA2 are fixed-term, compared to about 29 percent at ESSALUD1. The physical resources per doctor appear to be twice as large in

Table 5.2 Selected Characteristics of Sample Hospitals (1998)

Hospital	MINSA1	MINSA2	ESSALUD1	Private1
Beds	**304**	**435**	**1,471**	**101**
Doctors	122	345	670	83
Appointed	79	212	476	n.a.
Fixed-term	43	133	194	n.a.
Medical consultations (1995)	102,411	141,292	438,004	86,275
Deliveries	6,265	3,726	8399	248
Natural	4,421	2,897	3,428	55
Cesarean	1,844	829	4,971	193
Indicators				
Beds/doctor	2.5	1.3	2.2	1.2
Contractual share (%)	35.2	38.6	29.0	—
Consultations/doctor/year	839	410	654	1,039
Deliveries per doctor	51	11	13	3
Share of Cesareans (%)	29.4	22.2	59.2	77.8

Sources: The Statistical Offices of MINSA1 and MINSA2; the Office of the Medical Director for Private1; and II Census of Hospital Infrastructure of Health Structure, Ministry of Health, Office of Statistics and Informatics.

Note: Unavailable data is signified by *n.a.*

MINSA1 and ESSALUD1 as in the other two hospitals, while the number of consultations per doctor is highest at Private1 and at MINSA1. MINSA1 leads the other hospitals by far in the number of deliveries per doctor, which is to be expected given its specialty in maternal care. Interestingly the share of Cesareans is highest at Private1, followed by ESSALUD1, despite the fact that their patients tend to come from higher socioeconomic classes, and hence from lower-risk populations.

Conceptual Framework and Hypotheses: Corruption, Institutions, and Agents

The term *corruption* covers a very broad set of practices that include the illegal use of goods and services for the benefit of an agent or the people that he or she favors. Although corruption is a universal problem, it tends to be more common and more serious in developing countries, where institutions are generally weak (Rose-Ackerman, 1998: 35). The organization Transparency International (1996) reported that no country was free of corruption. The World Bank has estimated that the annual value of bribes globally could exceed US$80 billion (Walsh, 1998).

Many recent studies have emphasized the effects of corruption on economic development, resulting in a poor allocation of resources, a reduction in agents' confidence, and higher levels of inefficiency. Daniel Kaufmann, a senior economist with the World Bank, is quoted by Walsh (1998) as maintaining that corruption has a negative impact on all development indicators: economic growth, internal and external investment, and poverty. Bardhan (1997) states that occasionally corruption can lead to improved economic efficiency, e.g., when individuals pay influential bureaucrats in order to obtain services more promptly. But in the long term, the results of corruption are difficult to control because of the arbitrary and uncertain conditions they create for many of the agents.

The literature on the diagnosis and control of corruption is still emerging. The approaches thus far have attempted to answer the question of how to prevent corruption. These studies fall into two groups, one emphasizing individuals and the other emphasizing institutions. Without rejecting the contribution of the first approach, which stresses mechanisms for penalizing corrupt practices and agents, this study adopts the institutional approach, which seeks to identify the factors that foster corrupt practices in organizations.

This theoretical perspective holds that institutions set the ground rules, formal and informal, of human interaction. Formal rules include procedures, laws, and regulations. Informal rules include accepted norms, codes of behavior, or social conventions, among others (North, 1990). Equally important are the mechanisms that enforce both types of rules and make them effective. Institutional analysis of corruption reveals that it is more difficult to prevent malfeasance when mechanisms that generate adequate incentives are absent. Institutions have a great influence on workers' behavior; "an organization can be negligent even though its workers are not."[4]

To analyze the impact of institutions on corruption, it is useful to think within the framework of the "principal-agent" problem. A principal is any actor who delegates functions to an agent. If we think of individuals within these institutions as agents who try to maximize their own welfare within available opportunities and existing restrictions, then one of the most important potential constraints to corrupt behavior is the set of institutional rules governing the workplace and contracts. Agents are also affected by the availability of information and by their own capacities and resources. The structure of incentives does not necessarily motivate the agent to act in the best interests of the principal. In fact the central problem is that information asymmetry prevents the principal from effectively monitoring and evaluating their agents' efforts or compliance with work contracts.[5]

Caiden and Caiden (1988) maintains that any badly designed institutional system generates opportunities for corruption. The author divides systems into three categories: (1) formal procedures that indicate how public administration should work; (2) informal practices that indicate how workers really behave; and (3) the management or administration itself, which indicate how the work and actions of an institution's officers are ordered and controlled. Thus the important factors are a set of formal rules (laws, contracts, regulations) that regulate the actions of agents and the informal rules determined, for example, by the social context.

With respect to the formal rules, it is assumed that agents guide their actions partly by the objectives and procedures established in the rules, and partly for their own reasons, according to the degree of flexibility permitted

---

[4] Klitgaard (1992) quoted by Mosqueira (1995).
[5] For a synthesis of the literature see Pratt and Zeckhauser (1985) and Arrow (1985).

by the rules. Such flexibility depends, in turn, upon the procedures for monitoring agents' actions and the mechanisms for reprimand or reward. The social context (informal rules) also plays an important part in agents' incentives. Aspects such as the value that the social environment places on effort and honesty, and worker beliefs (for example, the belief that promotion depends more on length of service than on merit) have an important impact on agents' actions.

Klitgaard (1990) provides a working approximation for analyzing systemic corruption and making recommendations on how to control it. The author's approach is illustrated by the following equation:

$$C = M + D - T \qquad [5.1]$$

where C is corruption, M is monopoly, D is discretionary authority, and T is transparency. That is, the probability of corruption increases if the activity in question is a monopoly, if officials have broad discretionary authority, and if their functions are exercised with little transparency. The implications are clear: Reduce monopoly situations, limit officials' discretionary power to only what is needed to do the job effectively, and increase transparency. Evidently, it will not always be feasible to prevent a monopoly (e.g., in customs control at airports). In this case the strategy should be based on curbing discretionary powers (the choice of which luggage will be inspected) and increasing transparency (clear information to passengers about what is allowed and inspections in full public view).

Two other factors are important in explaining systemic corruption: impunity and the low pay of public officials (Rose Ackerman, 1986; Klitgaard, 1990; Gray, 1979; among others). Both create conditions that foster corruption. As long as the risk of conviction for malfeasance is low and the possible benefit to be obtained is high, the temptation of corruption will always be strongly present. Joan Prats and Julia Company (1996) of the Barcelona Governance Project distinguish between systemic corruption and behavioral (*conductual*) corruption. The former refers to factors or failures in the system that predispose corruption and the latter to the opportunistic conduct of isolated individuals. This distinction is useful since it leads to different strategies. If corruption in a society occurs in isolated cases, imposing harsher penalties through judicial action is a viable strategy. But if the corruption is systemic, because the economic and political ground rules facilitate its growth, a judicial solution is ineffective because when corrupt officials are processed and convicted, the system creates others (Ocampo, 1993).

An orderly way of analyzing this subject starts with the following equation of Compatible Incentives, defined as:[6]

$$I = (1-q)(w+c) - qF \qquad [5.2]$$

where I represents an agent's total expected income from committing a corrupt act, w is the agent's legal income, q is the probability of detection, c is corrupt income, and F is the effective penalty.

Thus if the agent's legal income (w) is less than the total expected income from a corrupt act (I), the agent will have an incentive to engage in corrupt practices. The definition of I includes the probability of detection of a corrupt act (q_1), and the penalty (F) upon detection. Thus, q and F represent the effectiveness of the mechanisms of control and punishment in the environment in which the official works. With a low q or F, I increases and with it the probability that it is greater than w. The official will then have more incentives to engage in corrupt practices. If q and F are high, I will be lower, which reduces the incentive for corruption. This is determined at the level of w. If w is low, the probability increases that w is less than I, and therefore the incentive to engage in corrupt practices increases.

To use this framework, it is necessary to identify specific kinds of corrupt activity and relate each to its institutional context. However most studies that seek to establish a typology of corruption are based not on specific types of corruption but on more-general effects related to the amount of bribes and the level of competition between public agencies.[7]

The specific case of hospitals, however, allows a more precise typology that identifies three general levels of corruption. The first level, *major corruption*, occurs when public agents use their positions of public authority to benefit from decisions associated with construction, rehabilitation, and purchases of expensive equipment in hospitals. The second level, *medium corruption*, occurs when public agents benefit from the use of hospital services, inappropriate use of the facilities provided by the organization, absentee-

---

[6] The equation relates to one proposed in the work of Di Tella (1997) although it is not reproduced exactly.

[7] See for example Shleifer and Vishny (1993).

ism, and graft in less-expensive purchases of equipment and common supplies. The third level, *petty corruption*, is associated with the collection by staff members of bribes from patients. Within the latter two categories, one can be even more specific and focus on five types of corruption: (1) absenteeism, (2) theft of inputs, (3) improper charging of patients, (4) improper charges to influence the purchase of equipment and other supplies, and (5) provision of unnecessary services. This chapter concentrates on two of these: absenteeism, and provision of unnecessary services.

Absenteeism

Absenteeism is defined as the use of working hours, paid by the hospital, for personal activities inside or outside the work center. This includes leisure activities (conversations in the cafeteria, rest during work time, etc.) that do not increase income, and private practice or other better-remunerated activities that do. This latter type of absenteeism should be affected by any deficiencies in staff control mechanisms as well as by the opportunity costs for doctors. Since fixed-term doctors can be penalized more readily than appointed doctors by simply not renewing their contracts, Hypothesis 1 posits that *absenteeism is more common among appointed doctors than fixed-term doctors.*

This hypothesis can be described precisely in the framework of the equation of compatible incentives [5.2] presented earlier. The probability of detection (q) and the level of legal income (w) can be considered as equivalent for appointed and fixed-term doctors.[8] But since appointed doctors have likely been working longer, they are likely to have more private patients, which means that their income from absenteeism (the measure of corruption in this case) or the opportunity cost of remaining in the hospital will also be higher. Additionally, the likelihood of dismissal as the effective penalty (F) is greater for fixed-term doctors. Therefore, it is more probable that w is less than I for appointed doctors than for fixed-term doctors. For this reason, greater absenteeism is expected among appointed doctors.

---

[8] In principle, legislation stipulates that wages are basically equivalent; although in practice, some legally unforeseen differences could occur (bonuses in kind from the hospital's own income).

Induced Demand: When Doctors Provide Unnecessary Treatments

Unnecessary health services — treatments that exceed the protocol for what is needed — can be viewed as corrupt when the health service provider encourages them for his or her own benefit. To analyze this phenomenon, data on hospital births was analyzed with the expectation, based on the wider literature, that some of the Cesarean deliveries performed were not technically indicated. Since doctors or facilities can benefit from a Cesarean delivery — through additional revenue or a more convenient schedule — nonmedical factors could influence whether or not a woman gives birth to her child vaginally or through surgery.

For some years, the study of Cesareans has centered on analysis of the incentives for patients to submit to them and for doctors to perform them. Several studies have found different motivations for doctors to perform Cesarean deliveries. For example, Keppel et al. (1982) found that mothers covered by private insurance have a high rate of Cesareans, while mothers who pay out of pocket have the lowest rate. The most common explanation is the hypothesis of supplier-induced demand. That is, in certain market conditions — usually an excess supply of doctors — physicians use their authority to prescribe additional treatments for their patients, thereby avoiding a reduction in their incomes by generating additional demand for their services (Tussing and Wojtowycz, 1992: 531).

A common criticism of studies singling out economic motivations for Cesarean deliveries has been the limited use of control variables in their estimates. Consequently other research has emphasized the importance of controlling the results with characteristics of the hospitals and doctors. The works of Tussing and Wojtowycz (1992 and 1993), for example, offer different explanations for the high rates of Cesarean deliveries (in New York City), which include changes in medical training, the effects of malpractice claims on doctors' conduct, and technological change. The authors ascribe two types of economic motivation for Cesarean deliveries: fear of malpractice actions (obstetricians often perform C-sections to minimize the risk of being sued for negligence), and higher income or self-interest.

Although the first reason does not apply in the Peruvian context, the second — obtaining higher income or furthering self-interest — could be important. Adapting the Tussing and Wojtowycz model, this study proposes that the income (or benefit) expected by a doctor from the corrupt practice of performing an unnecessary Cesarean is principally related to two variables: (1) monetary income (in private hospitals), and (2) convenience or free time (in public hospitals).

This leads to Hypothesis 2 of the study: *Because of its effect on income, the ratio of Cesareans to total births is higher in private clinics than in the ESSALUD and MINSA hospitals.* The hypothesis is based on the fact that, given the system of reimbursement by insurance companies, Cesareans and additional or more-complex care result in higher income for a private facility (but not for the public hospitals). In addition, both patients and doctors in Peru are affected by a lack of information and the almost complete absence of regulated standard medical procedures.

We can assume that the probability of detection (q) and the effective penalty (F) in all three organizations are similar. Peruvian rules and regulations in the health sector are not well enforced, even in cases of malpractice. Therefore the important determinant is probably the variable related to income from corruption (c). In this case, the income from committing a corrupt act (performing an unnecessary Cesarean delivery) can be very high for clinics (but not for public hospitals), giving them more incentives to engage in this type of malfeasance.

Hypothesis 3 holds that *the ratio of Cesareans to total births is higher in ESSALUD hospitals than in MINSA hospitals because of the procedure's effects on the convenience of doctors.* This hypothesis is based on the fact that doctors in ESSALUD hospitals are able to schedule their visits and treatments, whereas doctors in MINSA hospitals cannot. Thus ESSALUD doctors can prescribe Cesareans, even when they are not technically indicated, for their own scheduling convenience. In terms of the previous equation, the income from corruption (c) can be considered to include nonmonetary benefits (e.g., an uninterrupted weekend).

The studies by Tussing and Wojtowycz caution about the importance of including certain kinds of control factors, particularly in a hypothesis like this one in which the different rates of risk between the populations served by sample hospitals could also explain differences in outcome. In particular MINSA patients tend to come from lower socioeconomic levels than patients in the ESSALUD hospitals. Consequently a higher proportion of MINSA patients are unlikely to have received proper care during pregnancy.

This increases the possibility of problems at the time of birth and the need for Cesarean deliveries. As a result of this factor, the ratio of Cesareans to total births should be higher in MINSA than in ESSALUD hospitals (and higher in the ESSALUD hospitals than in private facilities, which tend to serve an even higher social strata).

Lastly, Hypothesis 4 of the study expects that the *ratio of Cesareans to total births is higher for appointed doctors than for fixed-term doctors*. As with the hypothesis for absenteeism, the principal factor underlying this hypothesis is the ease with which fixed-term doctors can be penalized. Income from committing a corrupt act plays a less important role. In terms of the equation of compatible incentives [5.2], c is similar for both groups, while F is lower for appointed doctors, which generates more incentives for them to engage in corrupt practices.

Methodologies for Analyzing Absenteeism and Induced Demand

To obtain empirical information on absenteeism, surveys were conducted of patients, doctors, and nurses in each of the four hospitals. In Private1, a reduced version of the survey was used for doctors, eliminating questions that did not apply to the private sector.

The total sample contained 576 doctors, of which 246 worked in ESSALUD1, 186 in MINSA2, 94 in MINSA1 and 50 in Private1. The survey covered 462 nurses in the three public hospitals, of which 238 worked in ESSALUD1, 163 in MINSA2, and 61 in MINSA1. Lastly, 229 outpatients were interviewed (97 from ESSALUD1, 72 from MINSA2, and 60 from MINSA1) and 95 admission patients (37 from ESSALUD1, 32 from MINSA2, and 26 from MINSA1).

The size of the survey samples was calculated to obtain results with a 4 percent margin of error and a confidence level of 95 percent. For patients, the calculation of the sample took into consideration data on the number of users who daily attend outpatient departments as well as those who were hospitalized, as reported in the *II Census of Health Sector Infrastructure and Resources* (Ministerio de Salud, Peru, 1996). The surveys of doctors and nurses were also structured on the basis of this census data, and an approximate ratio of the proportion of appointed and fixed-term staff. Survey respondents were chosen at random from each hospital's list of personnel. Interviews were also conducted with high-level officials (directors, deputy directors, heads of personnel, head nurses, and heads of pharmacy) in the four hospitals to obtain the qualitative information necessary to supplement and interpret survey data.

In the analysis of Cesareans as a form of induced demand, information was collected on each birth in 1998 in three of the four hospitals participating in the study. MINSA1 was excluded because it specializes in maternity-children's care, and therefore treats a large number of complex cases that could bias the results, and because of difficulties in accessing the data. Complete information was obtained for the other three hospitals, except for November and December in the case of MINSA2. In addition, a number of files were incomplete. Thus the final number of observations differs from the number of births registered by each hospital. Most of these exclusions relate to the records of MINSA2.

For the three hospitals in this part of the study, access to the records was uneven. It was open for all the medical records of patients treated in ESSALUD1 and in Private1. As mentioned, access was incomplete for MINSA2; only 2,009 records of the 3,726 births registered could be used.

The analysis follows the methodology proposed by Tussing and Wojtowycz (1992 and 1993) who use a probit model in which the dependent variable is the birth delivery method, with value 0 for a vaginal delivery and 1 for a Cesarean. The independent variables represent characteristics of the mother, her medical condition, and the hospital. The basic intent of the analysis is to estimate the influence of institutional variables on the probability that the delivery is Cesarean, controlling for different medical variables. Presumably institutional variables would have had no measurable impact if the decision between vaginal delivery and C-section were based solely on medical considerations.

The variables used can be divided into three groups:

♦ Medical control variables (mother's age, gestational age of fetus, weight of fetus, number of previous pregnancies, etc.),

♦ Institutional variables of the hospitals (employment status of the doctor who attended the delivery, ownership system of hospital where it took place), and a

♦ Variable on the convenience for the doctor (date of the delivery is defined as 1 on a weekend or holiday and 0 for the rest).

Estimates of Corruption in Peru's Hospitals

This section begins with an overview of the kinds of problems that medical personnel, patients, and directors perceive to be most common in the four hospitals. It also presents important information regarding the institutional differences between the hospitals. Although the four hospitals do not constitute a representative sample of Peru's hospital sector, the problems identified appear to be common in the hospitals of metropolitan Lima.

Many respondents identified *lack of transparency in decision-making* as a problem in managing the hospitals. Transparent decision-making is closely related to the degree of communication between administrators and managers and the organizational staff. Regardless of the efficiency and wisdom of management decisions, if they are not discussed or communicated to the hospital staff, they lack transparency and, as mentioned in the theoretical section, create a more favorable environment for corruption.

Communication problems are frequent in the hospitals (see Table 5.3). A high percentage of the surveyed doctors and nurses were either unaware of management instruments or mistaken about their existence.[9] More than 57 percent of all doctors answered incorrectly or that they "didn't know" when asked if their hospital had "expenditure agreements" or written institutional mission statements. But the rate varied strongly across hospitals. For example, correct knowledge about the existence of a written institutional mission statement was highest in ESSALUD1, followed by MINSA1 and MINSA2; while Private1 doctors responded incorrectly much more often.

Similarly, though 39 percent of doctors were unaware of or mistaken about operational targets, this varied significantly among hospitals, with shares of 43 percent in MINSA1, 30 percent in MINSA2, and 18 percent in ESSALUD1. But communication problems were also observed in Private1, which in every case had a higher share of doctors who were unaware or mistaken about management instruments than did any of the public hospitals. For example an astounding two-thirds (66 percent) of the private facility's doctors were either mistaken or unaware of the existence of operational targets.

---

[9] Doctors and nurses responded similarly; to simplify discussion, only doctors' responses are reported here.

Table 5.3 Communication with Doctors Regarding Management Instruments

	Formal information	According to doctors		
		Yes (%)	No (%)	Don't know (%)
MINSA1				
Institutional development plan	YES	60	17	23
Income and expenditure budget	YES	70	5	25
Expenditure agreements	YES	34	13	53
Operational targets	YES	57	13	30
Written statement of institutional mission	YES	48	20	32
Mechanisms for personnel evaluation	YES	52	25	23
MINSA2				
Institutional development plan	YES	64	11	25
Income and expenditure budget	YES	79	2	19
Expenditure agreements	YES	44	6	50
Operational targets	YES	70	6	24
Written statement of institutional mission	NO	38	10	52
Mechanisms for personnel evaluation	YES	60	20	20
ESSALUD1				
Institutional development plan	YES	82	1	17
Income and expenditure budget	YES	86	3	11
Expenditure agreements	YES	55	5	40
Operational targets	YES	82	4	14
Written statement of institutional mission	YES	68	4	28
Mechanisms for personnel evaluation	NO	78	9	13
Private1				
Institutional development plan	YES	40	26	34
Income and expenditure budget	YES	62	6	32
Expenditure agreements	YES	36	12	52
Operational targets	YES	34	22	44
Written statement of institutional mission	YES	18	20	62
Mechanisms for personnel evaluation	YES	40	30	30

Source: Instituto APOYO survey of doctors in four metropolitan Lima hospitals.

Notes: Formal information comes from interviews with members of the hospitals' administrative management teams. The final three columns report doctors' responses to the question, "Does the hospital have the following management instruments?" Interpretation of personnel evaluation instruments in ESSALUD1 is complicated by the fact that the hospital was in the process of implementing such a system during the study, even though there was no formal mechanism in the ESSALUD central office.

When asked directly about lack of transparency in procurement and hiring, a substantial number of respondents answered affirmatively. Thirty-two percent of public-sector doctors reported that lack of transparency was either common or very common in procurement of hospital supplies. Slightly less, about 28 percent, said that low transparency was common or very common in the contracting processes. The differences among hospitals were somewhat surprising in that a higher percentage of doctors considered lack of transparency as either common or very common in ESSALUD1 when that hospital had the lowest awareness of the existence of such a management mechanism. ESSALUD1 was followed, in order, by MINSA1 and MINSA2 where, again, reports of lack of transparency were in inverse proportion to the share who were aware of such oversight mechanisms.

The term "lack of transparency" was associated implicitly in the questionnaire with irregular or corrupt action, particularly through linkage to questions about the probability of punishment. Penalties for lack of transparency in procurement and hiring were perceived to be most severe in ESSALUD1, followed by MINSA2, with MINSA1 in third place (see Table 5.4). Asked, "What would happen if it were discovered that purchases of supplies lacked transparency?" 33 percent of sample doctors in ESSALUD1

Table 5.4 Doctors' Perceptions of Imposed Penalties (In percent)

	Dismissal	Fine	Warning	Nothing	Unsure
Penalties for lack of transparency in input purchases					
Public sector	24	5	28	22	21
MINSA1	10	4	42	23	21
MINSA2	19	5	32	19	25
ESSALUD1	33	5	21	23	18
Penalties for lack of transparency in personnel hiring					
Public sector	17	3	22	25	33
MINSA1	10	2	33	27	28
MINSA2	15	3	26	20	36
ESSALUD1	22	3	13	27	35

Source: Instituto APOYO survey of doctors in four metropolitan Lima hospitals.

Notes: All the differences among hospitals are statistically significant, except in the case of "fine(s)" and the residual category (i.e., "don't know" or "unsure").

thought the result would be dismissal. Only 19 percent of doctors in MINSA2 and a mere 10 percent of doctors in MINSA1 expected such a dire outcome in their institutions. However, at the other extreme, a similar and significant share of doctors in all three hospitals believed *nothing* would happen (23, 19, and 23 percent for MINSA1, MINSA 2, and ESSALUD1, respectively).

Based on this pattern of relative impunity, one should not be surprised to find that corrupt practices are perceived to be more frequent in the MINSA hospitals than in ESSALUD1. When doctors were asked if they knew about the existence of activities by hospital workers that were illegal or violated the institution's own regulations, 48 percent of MINSA1 and 40 percent of MINSA2 doctors answered yes, compared to 29 percent at ESSALUD1. For the public sector as a whole, more than one-third of the doctors admitted knowing of irregular or corrupt activities.

Table 5.5 Doctors' Perceptions of Frequency of Theft and Improper Billing (In percent)

	Rare	Uncommon	Common	Very common	Unsure
Theft of supplies or work materials					
Public sector	53	24	14	7	2
MINSA1	35	40	22	2	0
MINSA2	52	22	13	9	4
ESSALUD1	60	20	11	7	2
Improper charging of patients for earlier or better treatment					
Public sector	71	17	6	3	3
MINSA1	77	18	5	0	0
MINSA2	62	19	10	3	6
ESSALUD1	76	14	4	4	2

Source: Instituto APOYO survey of doctors in four metropolitan Lima hospitals.

Notes: The response categories in Spanish were *"nada habitual," "poco habitual," "habitual," "muy habitual,"* and *"no sabe o no preciso."* All differences between hospitals in appraisals of supply theft are statistically significant, except in the following cases: between MINSA1 and MINSA2 in the categories "uncommon" and "common," and between MINSA2 and ESSALUD1 in the category "very common." For improper charging of patients, the only differences not statistically significant are between MINSA2 and ESSALUD1 for "uncommon" and "common," between MINSA1 and MINSA2 for "very common," and between MINSA1 and ESSALUD1, also for "very common."

Supply theft was identified as the most widespread form of corruption (see Table 5.5). In the public sector, 14 percent of doctors perceived it to be "common," and 7 percent called it "very common." This perception was highest in MINSA1, where 22 percent of doctors thought supply theft was common and 2 percent very common. The responses for MINSA2 were 13 and 9 percent, respectively, followed by ESSALUD1's 11 and 7 percent, respectively.

Surveyed doctors did not think bribery or improper billing for services was widespread (see Table 5.5). Only 6 percent and 3 percent of public-sector doctors perceived bribes to be a "common" or a "very common" problem, respectively. However some 23 percent of patients answering the question, "Were you asked to pay a bribe to get treatment?" said yes (see Table 5.6). The highest share of affirmations was in MINSA1 (30 percent), followed by MINSA2 (19 percent) and, finally, ESSALUD1 (16 percent). Overall, 74 percent of patients from whom bribes were solicited agreed to pay.

Perceptions of Absenteeism and Its Characteristics

According to specialists and workers in the sector, the problem of absenteeism is widespread in Peru's public hospitals. For example the deputy director of MINSA2 said: "... all hospitals must have this problem; doctors have other jobs because their pay is very low." Surveys results from doctors and nurses confirmed this opinion. Twelve percent of the doctors agreed that "the use of working hours for personal activities, or absence from work, was very common," while 22 percent believed it was "common." Thirteen per-

Table 5.6 Frequency of Patients Being Solicited for and Paying Bribes

	Yes		No	
	Number	%	Number	%
Were you asked for a bribe to get treatment?	53	23	176	77
If "Yes": Did you pay a bribe to get treatment?	39	74	14	25

Source: Instituto APOYO survey of patients in three public hospitals in metropolitan Lima.

Note: The difference between the percentages of patients who replied affirmatively and who replied negatively is statistically significant for both questions.

cent of nurses said that doctors' absenteeism was "very common" and 19 percent reported it as "common."

In a pattern that mirrors perceptions of theft, more respondents thought that absenteeism was a problem in MINSA1 than in either of the other two public hospitals. In particular, 18 percent of doctors in MINSA1 consider absenteeism to be "very common," compared to 12 percent of those in MINSA2 and 10 percent in ESSALUD1. More doctors perceived the problem as "common" in MINSA1 (35 percent) than in either MINSA2 (26 percent) or ESSALUD1 (13 percent). In stark contrast, only 4 of the 50 doctors interviewed in Private1 believed the problem of absenteeism to be fairly common. Since its reports of absenteeism were so rare, the private hospital was excluded, for simplicity, from subsequent analysis of this problem.

To analyze the extent of absenteeism among doctors, interviewees were presented with percentage ranges of the regulation hours that physicians actually work. Although very broad, the ranges give an approximate idea of hours lost through absenteeism by allowing one to estimate the percentage of regulation hours not worked (see Figure 5.2).

In MINSA1, doctors reported that staff physicians are present during only a little more than two-thirds of their contracted work shifts, and absent about 31 percent of the time. Nurses concurred, reporting that doctors missed

Figure 5.2 Survey Responses: Hours Absent from Work (In percent)

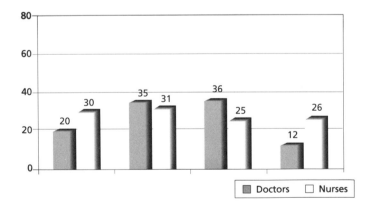

Source: Survey of doctors and nurses in 4 public-sector hospitals. Instituto APOYO.

Note: The differences are statistically significant except for those between MINSA1 and MINSA2 and between MINSA1 and ESSALUD.

35 percent of working hours. In MINSA2, doctors said they were absent 25 percent of the time, whereas the nurses' perception was significantly higher, some 36 percent. In ESSALUD1, the doctors reported that absenteeism accounted for about 12 percent of established work hours, while nurses reported the doctors were absent 26 percent of the time. Thus absenteeism in the perception of both doctors and nurses is more serious in MINSA1, followed in descending order by MINSA2 and ESSALUD1.

According to physicians in all the sample hospitals, appointed doctors are not only absent more frequently than fixed-term doctors, but also more than the rest of the medical and nonmedical staff. Of the total number of doctors surveyed, 35 percent classified absenteeism among appointed doctors as "frequent" or "very frequent." In contrast, only 6 percent considered absenteeism among fixed-term doctors to be "frequent" or "very frequent." Thus doctors themselves agree with Hypothesis 1, and the nurses share that perception.

Different Incentives: Fixed-Term Doctors versus Appointed Doctors

It was argued previously that potential income from failing to show up for work in the public hospital is higher among appointed doctors — since they can earn more than fixed-term doctors in their private practices. That is, appointed doctors have more experience and contacts, and consequently a higher probability of having outside patients, a private practice, and a position in a private facility. While 73 percent of the appointed doctors in the public hospitals stated they had an additional job outside their hospitals, the figure for fixed-term doctors was half as large, only 37 percent. Not only do younger doctors have less to lose by working their full hospital shifts, but the value in experience and contacts to be gained by being present is relatively higher than for older doctors who have already developed their networks.

Although specific figures are lacking to distinguish the external income of fixed-term and appointed doctors, age can be used to proxy this distinction. Fully 64 percent of appointed doctors are between 40 and 54 years old, compared to only 18 percent of fixed-term doctors.[10] And, in fact,

---

[10] Table 5.8 in Alcázar and Andrade (2000) reports the full age distribution. The doctor's university was originally used as a proxy to distinguish appointed and fixed term doctors, but no significant differences were found in this regard.

older doctors do earn more in the private sector than younger doctors (see Table 5.7). Almost 60 percent of doctors in the 40–54 age group earn more in the private sector, while the share for those in the 25–39 cohort is 50 percent.

With respect to the effectiveness of penalties (F), there do not appear to be significant differences between fixed-term and appointed doctors in terms of concern for severity of punishment when one is found to be unjustifiably absent. About two-thirds of the doctors in both groups think that a warning would be issued. Only 14 percent of appointed and 9 percent of fixed-term doctors thought a fine would be levied. And a mere 4 percent of both groups thought that dismissal was likely (see Table 5.8).

In response to a question about what caused absenteeism among medical staff, "low pay" was the principal reason cited by both appointed and contracted doctors (62 percent and 56 percent respectively). The second most importance cause was "absence of controls," with appointed doctors finding it more important than fixed-term doctors (20 percent versus 14 percent). The remainder in each group mentioned factors such as the lack of penalties and norms, among others. Appointed doctors apparently perceive less controls than do fixed-term doctors, which suggests that if a significant difference exists between the groups, then the concern about sanctions is higher among fixed-term than among "appointed" doctors.

Table 5.7 Doctors' Monthly Income by Sector and Age Group (In percent)

Age (years)	Under S/.1,400		S/. 1,400 to S/. 2,800		S/. 2,800 to S/. 3,500		over S/. 3,500	
	Public	Private	Public	Private	Public	Private	Public	Private
18–24	50	0	50	0	0	0	0	0
25–39	21	36	77	14	1	21	1	29
40–54	17	14	78	28	4	17	0	41
55 +	10	14	61	29	26	29	3	29

Source: Instituto APOYO survey of doctors in four Metropolitan Lima hospitals.

Notes: All the differences between wage groups, by age group, are statistically significant. The average foreign exchange rate in 1998 was US$1 equivalent to S/. 2.93.

Table 5.8 Doctor's Perceptions of Consequences for Being Caught Absent, by Job Status (In percent)

	Fixed-term	Appointed
Fine	9	14
Warning	69	63
Dismissal	4	4
Nothing	14	14
Unsure	4	5

Source: Instituto APOYO survey of doctors in four Metropolitan Lima hospitals.

Note: The differences between contracted and appointed doctors are not statistically significant except in the case of "warning."

Induced Demand: Cesarean versus Natural Deliveries

Analysis of Hypotheses 2 and 3, related to induced demand, is based on studying data of the ratio between Cesareans and total births. The monthly data for 1998 shows that ESSALUD1 led the other hospitals in the number of registered births (see Table 5.9). The two Ministry of Health hospitals both serve patients from a lower socioeconomic population than ESSALUD1's clientele. The patient sample was divided into four socioeconomic categories labeled A (the highest) through D (the lowest). In MINSA1, 81 percent of the patients surveyed belonged to the lower two socioeconomic categories. The corresponding figure for MINSA2 was slightly lower, about 70 percent. By contrast, in ESSALUD1, only one-third of patients came from the bottom two socioeconomic levels.

Thus one could expect that a higher percentage of births in the MINSA hospitals would require Cesarean deliveries since pregnant mothers from lower socioeconomic levels are less likely to receive adequate prenatal care (due to lack of resources and a lack of information about its importance). In ESSALUD1, by contrast, the pregnant mothers are insured, are more likely to come from a higher socioeconomic class, and are therefore also more likely to have received adequate prenatal care. This trend should be even more accentuated in Private1, which requires patients to be privately insured or to pay out-of-pocket. Yet despite the higher expected share of medi-

Table 5.9 Monthly Births by Sample Hospital (1998)

	Jan.	Feb.	Mar.	Apr.	May	June	July	Aug.	Sep.	Oct.	Nov.	Dec.
MINSA1												
Births	498	465	488	475	490	519	556	565	599	530	514	566
Natural (%)	74	78	71	73	75	73	73	72	67	67	60	66
Cesareans (%)	26	22	29	27	25	27	27	28	33	33	40	34
MINSA2												
Births	401	374	382	347	378	341	393	389	373	269	—	—
Natural (%)	78	84	79	78	78	80	80	71	74	87	—	—
Cesareans (%)	22	16	21	22	22	20	20	29	26	23	—	—
ESSALUD1												
Births	652	631	715	714	734	701	727	708	729	676	576	696
Natural (%)	53	54	50	57	56	50	53	52	55	51	46	49
Cesareans (%)	47	46	50	43	44	50	47	48	45	49	54	51
Private1												
Births	27	16	26	16	22	23	29	22	18	12	13	18
Natural (%)	37	19	19	19	26	26	28	9	28	17	8	22
Cesareans (%)	63	81	81	81	74	74	72	91	72	83	92	78

Sources: The Office of Statistics and Informatics in the public sector hospitals, the Obstetrics and Gynecology Department in Private 1.

Figure 5.3 Share of Cesarean Deliveries by Hospital, 1998 (In percent)

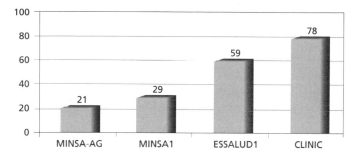

Source: Statistics offices in the public hospitals. Office of gynecology and obstetrics in the Clinic.
Note: All the differences between hospitals are statistically significant.

cally required Cesarean deliveries in the Ministry of Health hospitals, the actual distribution, as Table 5.9 and Figure 5.3 show, is the exact opposite.

The stark reversal of the expected pattern based on medical indications suggests that Hypotheses 2 and 3 may have some validity. The anomaly could be explained by additional factors related to the benefits received by doctors from determining the type of delivery. In the private hospital, where patients pay for the service directly or through private insurance indirectly, the main benefit to the doctor (or hospital) is the additional revenue derived from surgery.

In ESSALUD1, there is no difference in revenues, but doctors can still benefit from the added convenience of scheduling the delivery through Cesarean section rather than waiting for labor to begin.[11] Evidence about the timing of Cesarean deliveries supports this hypothesis to some extent. The

---

[11] The director of Obstetrics and Gynecology at ESSALUD1 mentioned in an interview that the rate of Cesareans in his hospital is high because the smaller ESSALUD hospitals are not able to treat all their pregnant patients. Pregnancies with complications and serious pathologies are referred to his hospital. [*Editor's Note*: Although the explanation may be true, the fact remains that a mountain of evidence from both developed and developing countries shows that the hospital's rate of Cesarean deliveries far exceeds the norm of what is medically necessary. Most experts estimate that the number of medically required Cesarean deliveries represents less than 10 percent of births].

ratio of Cesarean deliveries shows no particular pattern in MINSA1 and MINSA2 when comparing the shares before, during, and after holidays (see Table 5.10). By contrast there is a consistent trend in ESSALUD1 to perform more Cesareans in the three days prior to holidays. This could be at the request of the mother, but it could also be encouraged by doctors to reduce their holiday workloads.

Although the evidence appears to confirm Hypotheses 2 and 3, it would be more convincing if it also controlled for other possible explanatory factors, like medical risk, in a more precise way. In fact, an econometric analysis not only confirms the previous conclusions but also shows that institutional variables, such as the employment status of the doctor in public hospitals, are systematically associated with the decision to perform a Cesarean section.

The analysis follows Tussing and Wojtowycz (1992 and 1993), who analyze the probability of a Cesarean delivery using three groups of variables: (1) medical factors, (2) socioeconomic conditions of the mother, and (3) information on the hospital. In this study, the inclusion of medical variables and variables related to the socioeconomic characteristics of mothers was limited by access to information. The data were obtained from the medical records of the pregnant mothers and newborn infants in three of the four hospitals; however, these records did not include variables associated with the socioeconomic status of mothers. Important information was obtained for the inclusion of medical control variables. In addition

Table 5.10 Share of Cesarean Deliveries in Public Hospitals, Circa Holidays (1998) (In percent)

	April 9–12		July 26–29		December 24–27	
	Before	During	Before	During	Before	During
MINSA1	14	26	29	22	38	31
MINSA2	32	26	14	22	n.a.	n.a.
ESSALUD1	49	34	55	46	49	46

Sources: Office of Statistics and Informatics of MINSA1 and MINSA2, and the ESSALUD1 Obstetrics and Gynecology Department.

Notes: "Before" refers to the three days preceding the holiday. All the differences are statistically significant except in the last period for ESSALUD1. Not available is denoted by *n.a.*

to the control variables, the following variables were included to test our hypotheses:

♦ Ownership system of the hospital (to capture the effect of the different payment systems in each hospital, Hypothesis 2),

♦ Date of the delivery defined as a dichotomous variable equal to 1 if the birth takes place during a weekend and 0 otherwise (to capture the effect of scheduling deliveries associated with Hypothesis 3), and

♦ Employment status of the doctor attending the birth, whether appointed or fixed-term (to test Hypothesis 4).

To do this, the following equation was estimated as a probit model:

$$Pr \text{ (Cesarean Delivery)} = X_i B + \varepsilon_i \qquad [5.3]$$

where X is a vector of variables that include medical factors, characteristics of the hospitals, and characteristics of the doctors who attended the delivery; B is a vector of marginal effects; and ε is a stochastic error term.

Estimates were made using four distinct specifications. Three models were estimated for each health center (MINSA2, ESSALUD1, and Private1), focusing on the effect of the doctor's employment status and the effect of timing. In addition, a general model was estimated, including three of the hospitals, to analyze the influence of the ownership system on the probability of a Cesarean delivery. In the latter regression, it was not possible to include the employment status of the attending doctor since the system of appointed and fixed-term doctors is not used in the private sector. Similarly, it was not possible to include the gestational age and the number of previous pregnancies because this data was unavailable from the private hospital. Table 5.11 shows the marginal effects of each variable on the probability that the birth will be by Cesarean section.

In the general model, the control variables present the expected signs and are significant (see Table 5.11). For the gestational age of the fetus and its power squared, a likelihood ratio test was used to verify their joint significance (an F value of 67,011, statistically significant at the 0.5 percent level). Gestational age and its square are strongly associated with a higher probability of Cesarean delivery.

Women with multiple pregnancies are also more likely to have a Cesarean delivery, but the condition of the baby at birth (1 if the infant was healthy) reduces the probability of a Cesarean birth. The effect of birthweight on the probability of a Cesarean is ambiguous. A very heavy baby can generate complications in natural childbirth, which could require a C-section. On the other hand, a very small and/or premature baby may also require a Cesarean delivery. In this case, the joint significance test for both variables results in rejecting the possibility that the coefficients are equal to 0 (the likelihood ratio was 110,866, significant at the 0.01 percent level). It appears that higher birthweights are associated with lower probabilities of a Cesarean delivery, although the marginal effect declines as birthweight rises (indicated by a positive coefficient of 0.098).

In this general model, the variable associated with the hospital characteristics is the ownership regime. The regime is incorporated through three variables, each with value 1 if the hospital belongs to MINSA, ESSALUD, or the private sector, or 0 in other cases. When a delivery occurs in either the ESSALUD hospital or the private-sector facility, there is a greater probability of a Cesarean delivery, compared to the Ministry of Health hospitals, even after controlling for the other factors. This confirms Hypothesis 2; after controlling for other factors, the fact that Private1 has an incentive to encourage Cesarean deliveries leads to a higher probability of C-sections in that facility.

The econometric results also suggest that doctors may be scheduling deliveries for their own convenience. The possibility of scheduling deliveries on the days before a holiday or weekend allows doctors to reduce their workload on those days. As Table 5.11 shows, the probability of a Cesarean delivery on a weekend or holiday is negative, which indicates an accumulation of Cesareans on the preceding days (the marginal effect of this variable is −0.05).

In analyzing MINSA2 separately, we found that only some of the medical control variables were significant (the number of previous births, the cephalic circumference and its square, and the mother's age and its square). For mothers with previous pregnancies, the likelihood of having a Cesarean delivery is smaller, while the probability of a Cesarean delivery is higher for older women and for babies with larger heads.

Table 5.11 Factors in the Probability of a Cesarean Delivery (Marginal Effects)

	GENERAL MODEL		MINSA2		ESSALUD1		Private1	
Medical factors								
Mother's age	—		0.012*	1.55	-1×10^{-4}	-0.01	-1.306	-0.92
Mother's age^2	—		-7×10^{-5}	-0.57	**2×10^{-4}**	1.64	0.016	0.91
Previous pregnancies	—		-0.074*	-1.53	**-0.027**	-7.06	—	—
Gestational age	**0.231**	8.41	-0.032	-0.42	**0.129**	5.74		
Gestational age^2	**-0.003**	-8.93	2×10^{-4}	0.18	**-0.002**	-6.20		
Multiple pregnancy	**0.216**	4.49	0.09	0.77	**0.204**	4.22	—	—
Baby's condition at birth	**-0.335**	-6.89	—		**-0.384**	-8.11	—	—
Birthweight	**-0.638**	-10.20	-0.193	-1.16	**-0.673**	-9.36	-0.764	-0.90
Birthweight^2	**0.098**	10.01	0.028	1.08	**0.101**	8.99	0.081	0.65
Cephalic circumference	—		**0.160**	2.75	—		0.360	0.44
Cephalic circumference^2	—		**-2×10^{-3}**	-2.64	—		-0.004	-0.31
Institutional factors								
Doctor's empl. status	—		**0.846**	32.94	0.040	2.45	—	
ESSALUD hospital	**0.297**	6.39	—		—		—	
Private-sector clinic	**0.548**	12.36	—		—		—	
Doctor's convenience								
Weekend or holiday birth	-0.05	-4.38	-0.041*	-1.26	**-0.055**	-4.40	-0.037	-0.59
Chi^2	**578.42**		**1719.46**		**526.07**		**17.00**	
R^2 adjusted	0.039		0.642		0.045		0.067	
Number of observations	10,656		2,009		8,399		240	

Sources: The Office of Statistics and Informatics in the public-sector hospitals, the Obstetrics and Gynecology Department in Private1.

Notes: An asterisk indicates statistically significant at the 10% level. Boldface indicates statistically significant at the 5% level. T-statistics are in italics. In "general model," the reported coefficients indicate the marginal effect compared to being a Health Ministry hospital.

Although it has no medical explanation, the doctor's employment status is statistically correlated with the probability of a Cesarean delivery. A patient is more likely to have a Cesarean delivery when attended by an appointed doctor rather than a fixed-term doctor. This confirms Hypothesis 4, which posits that the ratio of Cesareans to total births is higher for appointed doctors than for fixed-term doctors because the latter are more closely monitored and subject to sanctions. Also, in this specification the day on which the birth occurs is statistically significant (at the 10 percent level).

Analysis of ESSALUD1 shows that most of the medical control variables are statistically significant and have the same signs as the general model. The joint significance tests for the variables with quadratic specifications show that all the pairs have joint significance in explaining the probability of a Cesarean delivery.

As in the MINSA2 estimate, doctor's employment status affects the probability of a Cesarean delivery. Patients attended by appointed doctors are more likely to have Cesarean sections than are those attended by fixed-term doctors. The marginal effect of the doctor's employment status is much larger in MINSA2 than in ESSALUD1 (0.846 versus 0.04). The marginal effect of the delivery date is also higher for ESSALUD1 than for MINSA2 (–0.055 versus –0.041). The effect of the doctor's employment status confirms Hypothesis 4. Thus, if an appointed doctor attends the birth, the probability of a Cesarean delivery rises.

Furthermore the estimate for the timing of the birth confirms Hypothesis 3, which posits that the ratio of Cesareans to total births is higher in ESSALUD hospitals than in MINSA hospitals because of the procedure's effects on the convenience of the doctor. In this case, the point estimate is –0.055, indicating that patients in ESSALUD1 are more likely to have a Cesarean delivery on a day that is neither a weekend nor a holiday. Additionally, this effect is larger and statistically stronger in ESSALUD1 than in MINSA2, where doctors are restricted in their ability to schedule deliveries.

Two other specifications were estimated in order to analyze the interaction of employment status and timing of deliveries. The difference between these models and the previous ones is that the variables relative to the delivery date and employment status were combined, creating four variables instead of two. The first variable takes a value of 1 when the delivery occurs on a weekend and was attended by an appointed doctor, and a value of 0 in the other cases. The second variable takes a value of 1 when the delivery occurs on a regular workday and was attended by an appointed doctor, and a value of 0 otherwise. Similarly, for the third and fourth variables a value of 1 is assigned when a fixed-term doctor attended the birth on a weekend or workday, respectively. These new calculations are intended to evaluate the difference in the relative weights of these two nonmedical factors — doctors' employment status and the date of delivery — on the probability of a Cesarean section, according to the public hospital where the birth takes place.

The results show that in MINSA2, the doctor's employment status has relatively greater importance in the probability of a Cesarean delivery. Thus births attended by appointed doctors, irrespective of whether it is a weekend or not, are more likely to be a Cesarean delivery. If the delivery is on a working day, the probability of a Cesarean also rises, but not as much. The marginal effect is 0.858 for workday deliveries attended by appointed doctors, 0.771 for weekend deliveries attended by appointed doctors, and –0.042 for workday deliveries attended by fixed-term doctors (see Table 5.12).

In contrast, for ESSALUD1 the date of delivery is of relatively greater importance. There a delivery on a working day has a higher probability of being Cesarean, irrespective of the employment status of the doctor attending the birth. If an appointed doctor is in attendance, the probability of a Cesarean is higher, but the impact of professional status is much smaller than the impact of the timing of the delivery. A delivery on a working day attended by an appointed doctor has a marginal effect of 0.101, followed by 0.065 if the delivery is on a working day attended by a fixed-term doctor and 0.048 if the birth is on a weekend attended by an appointed doctor. This is entirely consistent with Hypotheses 3 and 4 regarding the impact of incentives in inducing health services that are not medically indicated.

In the private hospital, none of the variables nor the chi-squared indicator was statistically significant. This seems to indicate that in Private1 other variables besides the medical and explanatory ones compared in these models could be influencing the probability of a Cesarean delivery. The failure of the model is understandable given that the percentage of Cesareans in Private1 is extremely high, close to 80 percent.

Conclusions and Recommendations

Public hospital corruption is a serious problem in Peru. Although this study concentrated on two specific types of malfeasance — absenteeism and pro-

Table 5.12 Factors in the Probability of a Cesarean Delivery (Marginal Effects), Additional Specifications

	MINSA2		ESSALUD1	
Medical factors				
Mother's age	0.007	*0.57*	-1×10^{-4}	*-0.01*
Mother's age^2	3×10^{-5}	*0.14*	2×10^{-4}*	*1.64*
Previous pregnancies	−0.183*	*−1.60*	**−0.027**	*−7.06*
Gestational age	−0.383	*−0.49*	**0.129**	*5.74*
Gestational age ^{2}	3×10^{-4}	*0.26*	**−0.002**	*−6.20*
Multiple pregnancy	0.093	*0.83*	**0.202**	*4.22*
Baby's condition at birth	—		**−0.384**	*−8.11*
Birthweight	−0.191	*−1.14*	**−0.674**	*−9.36*
Birthweight^2	0.028	*1.06*	**0.101**	*8.99*
Cephalic circumference	**0.158**	*2.68*	—	
Cephalic circumference^2	**−0.002**	*−2.58*	—	
Institutional factors				
Appointed x weekend	**0.771**	*17.99*	0.048*	*1.53*
Appointed x working day	**0.858**	*21.94*	**0.101**	*3.41*
Contracted x working day	**−0.042**	*−0.89*	**0.065**	*1.89*
Contracted x weekend (excl.)	—		—	
Chi-squared	**1725.27**		545.47	
R^2 Adjusted	0.644		0.047	
Number of observations	2,009		8,399	

Sources: The Office of Statistics and Informatics.

Notes: Asterisk indicates statistically significant at the 10 percent level. Boldface indicates statistically significant at the 5 percent level. T-statistics are in italics.

vision of unnecessary services — there is widespread perception of significant corruption. Some 36 percent of doctors surveyed in public hospitals said they knew of irregularities in their facilities. There also appears to be significant theft of supplies and improper billing of patients. Twenty-one percent of doctors in the public sector considered supply theft to be common or very common, and 9 percent had a similar perception about patients being charged improperly. Since only a few types of corruption were queried in the surveys, study findings do not preclude the existence of other types of wrongdoing.

Corrupt activities appear to be more frequent in MINSA1, followed by MINSA2 and ESSALUD1. For example, in these hospitals the share of doctors who said they were aware of corrupt activities was 48, 40, and 29 percent, respectively. The hospitals have important institutional differences that appear to be associated with differences in both the extent and types of corruption that were found. Corruption is most common in MINSA1, where control and penalty mechanisms are very inefficient. MINSA2, which recently changed its management processes in accord with the Programa de Administración de Acuerdos de Gestión (PAAG), came next. ESSALUD1, which operates under centralized management within the social insurance system, seems to be the least corrupt public hospital in the sample. This may indicate that centralized management and decision-making generate more-effective mechanisms of accountability.

All four hospitals, including the private-sector facility, suffer from communication problems. Large shares of doctors in each facility had a mistaken idea about or were unaware of the existence of a series of important management instruments. For example 40 percent of MINSA1 doctors answered incorrectly — or did not know — when they were asked if their hospital had an institutional development plan. The shares for MINSA2 and ESSALUD1 were 36 percent and 18 percent, respectively.

Absenteeism appears to be a major problem in public hospitals. The extent of absenteeism reported in each hospital appears to be strongly associated with two institutional factors: the high opportunity cost for doctors who work during established hours in the hospital, and the ineffectiveness of monitoring and penalty mechanisms. The evidence shows that absenteeism is much more common and more significant among appointed doctors than fixed-term doctors. Presumably this is because the appointed doctors have a stronger incentive to work outside the hospital since they have developed contacts and private practices that are lucrative. Appointed doctors are also less concerned about possible penalties for being absent since it is difficult to dismiss them, especially in contrast to the tenuous status of a fixed-term doctor whose contract can simply not be renewed. The general perception of inefficient control mechanisms in public-sector hospitals further reinforces that sense of security. At best the current system of registering attendance encourages doctors to show up for work, but it cannot assure that they stay for their entire shifts.

Evidently the public sector needs to implement a pay structure that rewards good performance, stimulates productivity, and improves the quality of services. Such measures would also improve patient care. However legal and budgetary restrictions make overnight changes in the pay structure difficult in the short-term. An alternative could be to introduce flexible working hours that would give doctors more freedom to engage in other activities. This could be accompanied by more-effective mechanisms of control and punishment for malfeasance. Indeed, experience suggests that pay raises rarely result in significant performance improvements unless they are accompanied by effective mechanisms to ensure accountability.

The study also showed that inducing demand for services beyond what is medically indicated was affected by pecuniary motives. The prospect of increased earnings apparently has a significant impact on the probability of Cesarean deliveries (even when the procedure may be to the patient's detriment). According to medical specialists natural birth is the healthiest way to deliver a baby, yet it is in ESSALUD1 and Private1, where health risks are less likely to occur, that the Cesarean rates are incredibly high. While it is possible that private-sector patients will ask doctors for a Cesarean section for their own convenience or because of fear of natural birth, the doctor bears responsibility for advising the woman regarding the medical necessity of a surgical birth. Indeed the doctor is the patient's principal source of information. To reduce this asymmetry of information between doctor and patient, the patient needs independent information regarding the advantages and disadvantages of natural and Cesarean delivery.

Other nonmedical institutional variables also appear to influence the decision to perform a Cesarean, even after controlling for medical factors. As with absenteeism, the doctor's employment status (whether appointed or fixed-term) is a significant factor in determining the likelihood of a C-section. In the ESSALUD hospital the variable indicating the doctor's convenience (whether the delivery occurred on a working day or a holiday) was also a significant factor, which illustrates the absence of mechanisms to regulate, control, and penalize inappropriate medical procedures.

CHAPTER 6

The Impact of Health Reforms on Irregularities in Bogota Hospitals

Ursula Giedion, Luis Gonzalo Morales,
and Olga Lucia Acosta

A survey of hospitals in Bogota, Colombia showed a wide range of irregular activities. About 5 percent of doctors' working hours in 1998 apparently were lost through unjustified absenteeism. About 60 percent of medical supplies in a sample were also purchased at higher prices than could be obtained through an organization used by district authorities to negotiate baseline prices with suppliers. All this took place within the context of Colombia's health-sector reform — a major change that increased population coverage through a new public-private scheme for providing health services. The evidence suggests that reform did not make substantial changes in the rules governing the sector in all cases. Yet the hospitals that seemed to be most successful in assimilating the reforms reported lower levels of irregular conduct as measured by an index constructed from data on supply prices.

Introduction

According to various international surveys, Colombia is a country plagued by corruption. The severity of the problem has been aggravated during the last two decades by the insinuation of drug trafficking into almost all spheres of society, especially in branches of public authority. A pervasive climate of tolerance of quick and easy enrichment has thrived at the expense of legality. For instance, an early 1990s survey found that 62 percent of Colombians thought "corruption is widespread or very widespread," and 32 percent "confess[ed] to having engaged in corrupt practices at some time in their life" (Vesga et al., 1992). In a recent survey of the business sector, firms admitted making payoffs of about 12.4 percent of the value of any contract they win (Fundación Corona, 2000).

Some observers of the health sector now contend that corruption is the principal problem facing the social security system (Thoene, 1999). For example, it was reported at the beginning of 2000 that the Health Superintendency was investigating funding irregularities in 20 of the 29 insurance companies that serve regular social security members.

Nonetheless hard evidence of corruption in the health sector is limited, and there has never been a systematic analysis. The only available data draws on the records of the Comptroller General of the Republic and the Health Superintendency. These records show that the health sector suffers from all forms of corruption, including various kinds of theft and fraud, as well as irregularities in public procedures, purchases of goods and services, bidding processes, and, more recently, the flow of public funds into private insurance companies. Some consider that this latest phenomenon is an unintended consequence of the change in ground rules from reforming the social security system (Thoene, 1999), which opened new spaces for corruption while reducing others. The capital city of Bogota offers an unrivaled opportunity for assessing how certain institutional innovations have affected irregular conduct in public hospitals. This is so for two reasons. First, the city has been in the vanguard of developing and implementing the health-sector reforms. Second, there has been considerable diversity in applying these innovations.

The District Health Secretariat, or Secretaría Distrital de la Salud (SDS), which coordinates the sector, was reorganized four times during the 1990s to facilitate decentralization and implement health-sector reform. By 1999, about 80 percent of the city's population was covered by health insurance provided by 24 of the nation's 28 largest insurance companies, and all of Bogota's public hospitals were operating under a legal status that gave them independence in key areas such as selling services and, to a lesser extent, hiring personnel. The sale of services to the private and public sectors generated 71 percent of public hospital funds.

This represents considerable progress, bearing in mind that only five years ago the poor population was entirely dependent on public assistance for health care, the hospitals were centrally managed by the Secretariat, and all funds were allocated on the basis of historical budgeting, irrespective of the quantity and quality of services provided.

Although reform has had its greatest impact in Bogotá, individual hospitals have implemented innovations at differing rates. For example some hospitals finance much of their operating budgets through service agreements with private insurers who cover the poor (with publicly subsidized premiums), while others still depend almost entirely on funds allocated directly by the SDS. Because of its size and range of participation in institutional reform, the district health system offers a rich context for studying how innovations affect irregular conduct in public hospitals.

Colombia's Health Reform and Institutional Innovation

In response to inequity, inefficiency, and poor quality in provision of services, Colombia embarked on a major reform of its health sector in 1993. At the time only 20 percent of the population was covered by health insurance, and doctors treated an average of fewer than two patients per hour — giving priority to curative over preventive treatments. Although there are no detailed studies of service quality in the public sector before the reform, it is significant to note that 40 percent of outpatient visits and 45 percent of hospitalizations in 1992 took place in the private health sector (Molina and Giedion, 1993). More disturbing yet, even people who were insured by the public social security agency preferred to use the services of private networks. In 1992, over 15 percent of rural and 35 percent of urban hospitalizations in private health centers involved patients who had health insurance financed by the State (Harvard School of Public Health, 1995).

It was clear from the start that low coverage was due less to the lack of resources than to poor management of funds and methods of allocation. Consequently health reform was designed to make radical changes in these areas. Direct public funding of public hospitals was to be gradually channeled through two kinds of conduits: Public and private insurers known as Empresas Promotoras de Salud (EPSs), or Health Promotion Firms, would cover people who could afford to pay premiums; and Administradoras del Régimen Subsidiado (ARSs), or Subsidized Scheme Administrators, would cover the poor. These organizations were expected to compete for members by negotiating good quality, low-cost service provision agreements with public and private health-service providers. The entire population would thus be covered in a General System of Health Social Security, with the right to choose between competing service providers (see Figure 6.1). The intention was to achieve universal coverage with a pre-established package of benefits.

Health reform involved several major institutional innovations for the public hospital sector. First, the new system of public resource allocation gradually replaced traditional budgeting. Hospitals would no longer receive their funds exclusively from the public sector but also from the sale of services to private insurers. The remaining public resources were to be disbursed against proof of actual service volume. The idea was to change the incentives faced by public hospitals in order to stimulate more efficient and transparent management through accountability to users who would reward or punish hospitals through consumer decisions.

Second, public hospitals were converted into Empresas Social del Estado (ESEs), or State Social Enterprises, an administrative status that conferred greater independence in managing human and financial resources while facilitating direct community control over hospital operations. As defined by Decree 1298 of 22 June 1994 (Art. 95), ESEs are a special category of public entity, "decentralized with legal status, their own capital,

Figure 6.1 Colombia's New Health Insurance System Based on Law 100

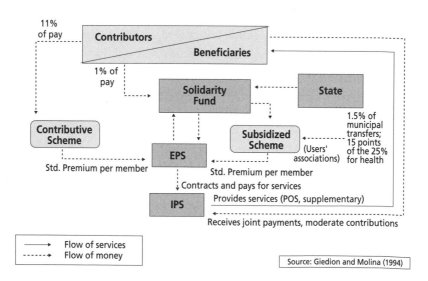

Source: Giedion and Molina (1994)

and administrative independence." Thus ESEs no longer depend on provincial governments (*entidades territoriales*) for the appointment of new officials.[1]

Third, boards of directors with broad community representation were created to have input in the appointment and removal of hospital directors, provide management oversight, and facilitate greater independence in hiring personnel. In effect, decisions once made by a central office (the District Secretariat) would now be made by individual boards made up of hospital officials, community delegates elected by users' associations responding to a public invitation to participate, and an SDS representative.

The expanded coverage achieved by the reforms thus far is indisputable. Approximately 60 percent of Colombians, including 75 percent of the poorest population, are now insured with a basic package of services. Over 200 ARSs nationwide offer services to poor people whose premiums are subsidized. In Bogota there are 30 ARSs competing for about one million members. In addition, all the more complex hospitals in the country and all the public hospitals in Bogota have become independent firms that purchase their own supplies, hire their own staff, and prepare their own budgets. Finally, it should be added that the reform also substantially increased the amount of funding, which made more-universal health coverage possible (see Table 6.1).

But implementation of the reform has encountered significant constraints. For example insurance coverage is financed largely from new funds, with only a very small part coming from reallocation of funds. Only 17 percent of the fiscal transfer from the central government — traditionally the principal source of financing for the public sector — has been "transformed" into demand subsidies that would flow into the ARSs. The remaining 83 percent of public funds are still channeled directly to public hospitals, which continue to allocate resources inefficiently. For example, in Bogota the less complex hospitals treat approximately 12 percent of the poor population

---

[1] According to the reform's explanatory statement, the principal modifications to the existing hospital model include a search for "independent, financially solvent, and decentralized [service provider] entities," with "independence" giving service providers "full capacity to act, contract, and assume obligations [and] to do this, the hospitals and other centers may become ESEs [with] their contracting processes subject to private law" (Ministerio de Salud, 1994). This was expected to give the hospitals more flexible management, which is a fundamental condition for competing with other providers, as was the intention of the 1993 reform.

Table 6.1 Selected Characteristics of the Health Sector for Colombia and Bogota

Indicators	Before reform (1993)		Five years later (1998)	
	Colombia	Bogota	Colombia	Bogota
Insured population as share of total (%)	24	30	60	81
Share of poor population covered by insurance (%)	0	0	75	88
Number of insurers in the contributive scheme	20	2	29	24
Number of insurers in the subsidized scheme	0	0	243	18
Total public health funds (millions of 1998 pesos)	1,512,127	171,586	3,654,012	318,753
Share of public funds allocated to health (%)	—	—	31	38

Notes: The contributive scheme category here includes social security for private-sector workers and public insurance for public employees. The exchange rate in 1998 was approximately US$1 = 1,426 Colombian pesos.

but receive a similar amount of funds as the ARSs that insure 82 percent of this population. Only 31 percent of total public health funds are allocated as demand subsidies; the rest continue to be allocated to support installed capacity. Due to pressure from various groups in the sector, the process of transforming these public funds has been frozen. Consequently the outlook for expanding insurance coverage and improving the benefits package for the poor population is very limited. Finally, a serious economic recession has aggravated the situation, pushing public hospitals into an unprecedented financial crisis.

Although the cited figures show that the changes in Colombia's health sector were well conceived, not all agents, especially the public hospitals, have been able to implement them fully and with maximum effectiveness. Public hospitals spend 70 percent of their budgets on personnel, but face restrictions on cutting costs because of inflexible labor legislation that protects workers. Moreover, the incentives for restructuring have been undermined because of the central government's vacillation on a speedy transition to the new scheme and because hospitals in crisis are regularly bailed out. In many cases, in fact, organizational changes have not produced new institutions.

Institutional Design and Irregular Conduct

By its nature, corruption is difficult to measure. Colombia is ranked among the countries with greatest evidence of corrupt practices. Corruption in the public sector, understood as the diversion of public funds for private purposes, has been documented year after year by audit agencies. The 1991 Constitution originated in the student movement's repudiation of traditional politics whereby individuals profited from public funds. In the opinion of some constitutional experts, the new Constitution overregulates public officials, reacting to endemic problems of corruption and patronage, long tolerated and fostered by the Congress of the Republic, with an excessive moralizing zeal.

The new Constitution was also an attempt to use public funds more efficiently by incorporating new principles into service provision that traditionally had been the exclusive preserve of the public sector. The legal development of these constitutional principles promoted links with the private sector in many public services and in social security.

The increased funding for health and the large number of new agents incorporated into this sector required very strong supervisory and control bodies, which have yet to be consolidated. Indeed, complaints of corruption have increased. Despite the furor, no study has been commissioned to systematically analyze the extent and scope of corruption in the sector.

This chapter represents a first attempt at that task, taking advantage of the fact that new ground rules introduced by the reform were not assimilated by all agents in the same way, making it possible to compare irregular conduct in reforming institutions with those still operating under traditional management guidelines. However, before continuing, it would be useful to review the types of corruption identified in public hospitals:

A first set of corrupt activities derives from the doctor-patient relationship. Many of these occur when doctors benefit from both a public-sector job and a parallel private practice. For example, doctors may improperly use public-sector facilities, equipment, or supplies to treat patients on a fee basis that generates additional income above and beyond that which they receive from the public hospital. This mixture of public and private sources of income also encourages absenteeism during hospital working hours. In addition to this "theft" of time, medical professionals may make improper use of facilities, equipment, or supplies to treat their private patients. Part of the

explanation given for this behavior is that professionals are paid fixed salaries in the public sector and hence lack incentives to dedicate their time and
energy to their public-sector jobs, especially when they have highly remunerative alternatives.

A second abuse of the doctor-patient relationship occurs when informal (under-the-table) payments are requested for certain services or for shorter
waiting times. This modality, which is frequent in the public hospital sector,
persists because of the chronic shortage of services and financial resources.

A third abuse of this relationship occurs when doctors induce patients to undergo unnecessary procedures. This problem is exacerbated
when doctors are paid by the type and number of services provided — a
fee-based system more characteristic of private than public practice. While
fixed salaries do not create incentives for inducing demand, a fee-for-service system can generate unnecessary demands, potentially endangering
the patient.

A fourth form of abuse occurs when health professionals improperly
refer patients to their own private practices for personal benefit. This behavior is known in the sector as "stealing patients," either from other professionals or from a hospital waiting list. A variation of this is to improperly
influence a patient to use the services of providers in which the professional
has a pecuniary interest or from which the professional receives benefits.

*A second set of corrupt activities derives from the hospital-payer rela-
tionship.* This involves falsification of bills, either by reporting services that
were never provided or by upgrading the reported severity of the case treated
(so-called "upcoding"). This problem, which was nonexistent under the historical budgeting system (since invoices were not generated), will become
increasingly important as more public hospitals are reimbursed for services
provided to the insured population. The Health Ministry is presently effect-
ing just such a change in the use of its funds for treating the noninsured
population. Although the new system has clear benefits in terms of incentives for higher productivity, it creates immense problems of control and
supervision since the National Health Superintendency has responsibility
for collecting and scrutinizing information on the services supplied by over
1,000 service providers around the country.

*A third set of corrupt activities derives from the hospital-supplier rela-
tionship.* This occurs when a hospital employee either requests or is offered
personal benefits by a medical supply or equipment company in exchange

for orders. The benefits may be passive (such as perquisites or unsolicited gifts) or active (a kickback). Similar corruption is common in other branches of the public sector. Since hospital supplies and equipment generally have very specific characteristics, suppliers use an infinite number of subtle mechanisms to influence the professionals who advise public agencies on the technical aspects of purchases. This is especially so when the purchase involves state-of-the-art medical technology in which the medical aspects can be used to override other considerations such as cost.

   A final set is a catchall of other corrupt activities. Unjustified absence of medical staff contracted to work a specified schedule in the hospital is also considered a form of corruption even when it is not related to enhancing a private practice. Such absenteeism is often tolerated, and justified socially as a consequence of the traditionally low pay of medical staff. Another very frequent form of corruption is open theft or pilferage of supplies by hospital staff. The high cost and small size of many hospital supplies means that workers can easily steal small quantities without being noticed. Stolen items can easily be charged to patients' accounts because the person who requests a supply is often the person responsible for administering it to the patient.

   To learn more about some of these types of corruption, surveys were administered to a representative sample of 32 hospitals. This chapter will focus, in particular, on unjustified absenteeism by doctors and overcharging for supply procurement.

Principal-Agent Theory and Combating Corruption

There is growing consensus that corruption levels are affected by the institutional factors that regulate the role of the hospital as an agent, and the roles of the community and Health Secretariat as principals (represented on the hospital boards). The framework of principal-agent theory helps explain how inefficiencies occur when principals delegate functions to agents, the objectives of the principal and agent diverge, and each party has access to different kinds of information about service provision and outputs.

   These inefficiencies decrease as the interests of the principal and agent become more closely aligned, and when transparency and accountability are strengthened. The latter are achieved through a combination of factors, including granting the agent *independence*, obtaining *information* on the agent's production, and granting *control* to interested parties.

The institutional innovations introduced into the public hospital sector in Colombia point precisely to these three elements: increasing the independence of the hospitals, linking delivery of public funds to services actually supplied rather than to inputs used, and creating hospital boards composed of the most important principals, i.e., the District Health Secretariat and the community. Each of these will be examined in turn.

A common view, not always well founded, holds that institutional *independence* for public officials (i.e., agents) is a good thing, although studies to assess this claim are only just beginning to bear results. More independent hospital management has several advantages, including the ability to make speedier decisions based on more information, increased local responsibility for institutional performance, and an enhanced capacity to improve an institution's general situation and financial standing (Walford, 1998). With these ideas in mind, one can hypothesize that greater hospital independence will generate a lower level of irregular conduct. Independent hospital directors theoretically have more incentive to control malfeasance since they are directly responsible for performance and have greater discretionary decision-making authority. Presumably, then, the two forms of irregular conduct that are the central subject of this chapter, the rate of absenteeism and the variation in supply prices, will be lower when the hospital has greater control over its human resources.

Even so, counterarguments against hospital independence can be made, based on the difficulty that the principal (in this case the hospital's governing body) has in monitoring the performance of its agent (e.g., the hospital director). The asymmetry of information between the board and the hospital director is very large. The complexity of hospital information and the relative ease with which it can be manipulated can prevent the principal from exercising adequate control over the agent. Clearly, independence cannot be evaluated apart from the mechanisms of accountability. In fact, greater independence could worsen corruption in the absence of monitoring, appropriate supervision and control mechanisms, or competition with other providers.

Real transparency, then, requires clear, complete, and timely *information* that enables the principal to monitor the agent's actions and decide if they are aligned with the principal's interests. How effectively information restrains irregular conduct depends on how data is used. The range extends from simply generating and publicizing information, to systems that collect and analyze data for allocating resources. In the context of this study, the existence of information and its use in constraining irregular conduct are clearly of central importance.

Merely collecting and publicizing information is generally not enough to insure meaningful transparency. Even an effective board of directors that has the required management tools, community representatives, and competition from other hospitals may not use information to control irregular conduct if that board is captured by special interests. Unless the board is effectively accountable to citizens, no amount of information will resolve the problem.

Efficient supervisory and *control* mechanisms are fundamental for combating irregular conduct. Without these mechanisms, it is impossible to convince anyone that there is a risk associated with illegal activities. These functions are exercised in different ways by different authorities within hospitals. Employees are formally monitored by their supervisors, who in turn are monitored by a department chief or the hospital director. Specialized internal units, such as control offices, external and statutory auditors, and comptrollers also frequently monitor staff, administrators, and institutional units. At the highest level, hospital activities are formally subject to review and auditing by the public-sector agency that is responsible for financial control.

These different levels of supervision, control, and penalty implementation require considerable coordination. After detecting an irregular act at any given level, penalties, although varied in character, can be a powerful control mechanism against corruption. However, to be effective oversight also requires objective information, transparent investigative procedures, and decisions impervious to manipulation.

Presumably the range of corrupt activity would be restricted more in an institutional environment with effective supervisory mechanisms whose transparency and effectiveness are respected by the community and considered to be legitimate. In sum, within the context of health reform, the amount of irregular conduct should be inversely related to the hospital's degree of independence, the availability of information, the principals' input into decision-making, and the existence of supervisory and control mechanisms.

Study Sources and Initial Findings[2]

Bogota was the first Colombian city in which the health reforms of the 1990s were intensively applied. For this reason, and because of the interest of the District Health Secretariat in improving its knowledge of the situation, it was decided to investigate the 32 hospitals in the SDS public network, building on the findings of an earlier study of efficiency also commissioned by the SDS (Giedion and Morales, 1997 and 1999).

First, key informants (i.e., the manager, administrative director, head of personnel, and head of internal disciplinary control) were interviewed in each hospital to assess implementation of the reform and explore the degree of independence, community participation, accountability, and internal and external supervision and control in each institution. Responses obtained from these interviews include perceptions as well as verifiable data. As far as possible the information given by the informants was cross-checked with corresponding records. The principal processes that were double-checked were staff hiring and supply purchasing. The interviews were also used to obtain direct information on the composition of the workforce in terms of employment status (permanent/contracted staff), the number and results of personnel assessments, the number of disciplinary processes initiated and completed, and the use of basic management tools.

Second, the processes involved in supply procurement were assessed by applying a "checklist" to determine if each hospital possessed the instruments and minimum conditions for transparency. Some items of this checklist included whether or not the hospital had kardex or documented purchase plans.

Third, surveys were undertaken, using two questionnaires in each hospital. The first was a survey of perceptions about the presence, frequency, and causes of certain types of corruption; the existence of supervisory and control mechanisms; and the attitude of officials when a violation was discovered. The survey was applied to a representative sample of the 8,256 medical and administrative officials in the district hospitals. An aggregate response rate of 95 percent was achieved, a very acceptable rate, especially for a self-reporting survey.

---

[2] This section describes the sources of information used in the chapter and offers a descriptive summary of survey results. For greater details, see Giedion et al. (2000).

The second survey was a census of head nurses in the public hospitals of Bogota that asked questions about "doctors' working hours" to determine the extent and implications of physician absenteeism; its possible causes; and the existence, operating capacity, and effectiveness of supervisory and control mechanisms designed to prevent such conduct. This survey was severely compromised by a group of nurses in several hospitals. Although 395 completed questionnaires were received, after critical review and validation only 130 of them were considered usable. Some nurses were reluctant to cooperate with the process, either out of solidarity with doctors or because they feared being branded as informers. In either case, this would imply that the real level of absenteeism is probably higher than the survey results indicate.

Fourth, a proxy was constructed for corrupt practices in the acquisition of medical-surgical supplies, using a review of all the 1998 procurement records for all the hospitals. This data was used to identify prices paid for six specific supplies, along with related information about the purchase (e.g., its date, and the form of payment). This review generated a validated database of 549 observations. Supplies were selected on the basis of criteria such as uniformity in character, quality, and use. Preference was also given to supplies that were purchased in large volumes compared to the institution's total purchases. The supplies selected under these criteria were Sodium Diclofenac SLN INY 75 mg/3 ml, Gentamicin SLN INY 80 mg/2 ml, lidocaine 15 S/E SOL INY 50 ml, powdered penicillin INY 1,000,000 UI, 5 ml disposable syringes C/A, and different sizes of latex examination gloves.

Secondary information was obtained from the public hospitals on characteristics of the purchase managers (e.g., gender, education, and length of service) and their incomes. Finally, information was also collected from the NGO Red Salud, which establishes reference baselines for supply purchase prices.

Perceptions of Corruption

In order to characterize the general perception of corruption in the district hospitals, an indicator was constructed from the survey of hospital personnel. The indicator was measured as the share of hospital staff members who stated they believed there was at least one form of irregular conduct in their hospital. The list of conducts included absenteeism, theft, procurement irregularities, informal payments for services, and improper use of facilities by staff. Fifty-five percent of the hospital staff in the survey of 32 district hospitals said that irregular conduct existed in their facility. In their opinion, the most frequent irregularities were noncompliance with working hours by doctors and bad management of supply procurement (see Table 6.2). In this regard, there were no significant differences among hospitals or between administrative and medical staff.

Compared with the situation before the reform, 59 percent of those surveyed thought that the frequency of irregular acts in public hospitals is now lower, while 27 percent did not perceive any change, and only 14 percent thought there was an increase. This is promising in the sense that, at least in the hospitals, perceived corruption seems to have declined, suggesting that the situation might have improved. Of course this is only one imperfect indication.

Guided by these results, further analysis focused on two forms of irregular conduct that were considered to be most common: bad manage-

Table 6.2 Most Common Forms of Irregularity in Public Hospitals

Are you aware of . . .	Yes (number)	Staff reporting irregularities (%)	Share of all staff (%)
Unjustified absence among medical staff	185	38	
Mismanagement of procurement	190	39	
Theft of material or equipment	78	16	
Unauthorized use of equipment, facilities, or supplies	24	5	
Unauthorized billing of patients	5	2	
Personnel who reported some irregular conduct	482	100	55
Personnel who reported no irregularities	395		44
No response	9		1
Total responses	886		100

Source: Survey of hospital staff perceptions regarding irregularities.

Note: Share of staff who reported irregular conduct has as its denominator the entire sample of hospital staff, including doctors, nurses, and administrative personnel.

ment of supply and equipment purchases, and unjustified failure of medical staff to fulfill their contracted working hours.

The main indicator of poorly managed supply procurement was the ratio between unit prices actually paid and the unit prices published by Red Salud. Red Salud is an NGO that has been contracted by the District Health Secretariat to negotiate agreements with pharmaceutical companies and distributors so as to lower the cost of procurement. Red Salud negotiates prices for about 185 medications and 9 medical-surgical inputs. The negotiated agreement is sent to the hospital directors and purchase managers in the 32 SDS hospitals, with all the necessary procurement information, including which medicines and inputs were negotiated, who are the suppliers, the agreed unit price, some possible discounts, and delivery schedules. The agreed price is valid for one year and does not change with the volume of purchases made by the hospital.

The resulting divergence of purchase prices from the reference baseline prices is significant for all six supplies that were analyzed (see Table 6.3 and Figure 6.2). With the exception of lidocaine, the average purchase prices are higher than the prices available to the hospitals through Red Salud's agreements.

It is unlikely that all the deviations are due to corruption in the handling of purchases. Poor management could also be responsible. Many hos-

Table 6.3 Price Data for Selected Medical Supplies (1998 Pesos)

Indicators	Penicillin	Syringes	Gloves	Diclofenac	Gentamicin	Lidocaine
Lowest price	260	49	66	170	36	410
Highest price	950	428	160	980	1,425	3,814
Ave. price	467	124	88	303	425	2,515
Standard deviation	167	43	15	127	282	1,069
Coef. of variation	0.36	0.35	0.18	0.42	0.66	0.43
Red Salud						
Reference price	392	105	69	195	298	2,573

Source: Authors' calculations based on 1998 district hospital procurement records and reference prices reported by Red Salud.

Note: For specific information about medical supplies, including units of purchase, see text. In 1998, the average exchange rate was US$1 = 1,426 Colombian pesos.

Figure 6.2 Distribution of Prices Paid for Selected Medical Supplies Relative to Reference Prices (In percent)

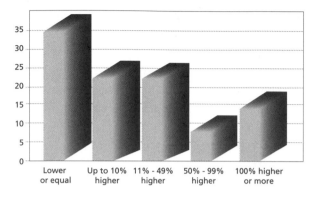

Note: Authors' calculations based on district hospital procurement records and Red Salud's reference prices for 1998.

pitals lack even the most rudimentary elements for managing procurement; so it is not surprising to find some directors justifying cost differentials on the grounds that the hospital "ran out of inventories and was forced to buy urgently needed supplies from the nearest pharmacy at very high prices" or "the hospital has no funds so the suppliers charge more."

Even so, presumption that these differences are due to irregularities is not unfounded. Indeed the media regularly reports charges and investigations of corruption in procurement. The accusations range from coverage of hospitals knowingly purchasing substandard supplies to instances in which purchase quantities are falsely padded in return for gifts or informal payments from contractors. Interviews with key informants also revealed the extreme weakness of the supervisory and control mechanisms for purchasing. This impression was reinforced by hospital survey results in which respondents identified irregular conduct in purchasing as one of the most common corrupt practices in their institutions.

The price distribution in SDS hospitals also suggests that graft is likely to be widespread in the procurement process. Only 34 percent of purchases were made at prices equal to or lower than the reference price. About 22 percent of purchases were within 10 percent of the reference price; but another 22 percent exceeded the baseline by 11 percent to 50 percent. Eight

Table 6.4 Estimated Corruption Costs in Bogota Public Hospital Procurement, 1998 (millions of Colombian pesos)

Medical supply item	Total value of purchases	Cost of purchases at reference prices	Difference
Diclofenac	21.1	17.6	3.5
Gentamicin	22.5	20.1	2.4
Lidocaine	35.8	34.5	1.2
Penicillin	27.6	29.6	(2.0)
Syringes	67.1	62.9	4.3
Gloves	309.0	262.3	46.7
Total	483.3	427.1	56.2

Source: See Table 6.3.

percent were at prices between 51 percent and 100 percent higher, and 14 percent were at prices more than 100 percent higher.

The magnitude of this irregular activity can be sensed by calculating how much money would be saved if all purchases were made at the reference price (see Table 6.4). If the six selected supplies were all bought at the prices negotiated through Red Salud, the hospitals would save Col\$ 56 million annually. This represents approximately 11 percent of the total spending on these selected supplies. Assuming that this percentage represents the average loss on purchases of all hospital inputs in one year, and given that supply spending represents about 10 percent of a hospital budget, the total loss for the City of Bogota would be approximately Col\$ 3,025 billion. This conservative estimate represents enough money to cover health expenses for an additional 24,000 members of the social security health plan.

Along with irregularities in purchases, unjustified absence by medical staff was the most commonly reported problem in the surveys. In the survey, 38 percent of those who reported irregularities reported that doctors were not complying with their work hours. These same staff estimated that doctors were, on average, unjustifiably absent 5.7 percent of the time.

Because of the previously cited difficulties encountered during the collection of information on doctor absenteeism, these figures probably underestimate the problem, which anecdotal evidence suggests is widespread. Bearing in mind these limitations, a conservative estimate of the direct annual cost of this phenomenon was calculated to be Col$ 2,575 million for Bogota, equivalent to approximately US$1 million or 1 percent of total district hospital spending. This figure may be the tip of an iceberg since medical staff salaries represent only one-fifth of personnel expenses, which account for some three-quarters of total hospital spending. If other staff were absent at the same rate reported for doctors, the total costs would be three to four times higher.

Of the nurses who completed the self-reporting survey, 61 percent responded that the most frequent form of absenteeism among doctors was "to arrive after the start of the shift"; 15 percent answered that doctors "leave before the end of the shift without justification," a situation often associated with multiple jobs and concurrent hours in different places.

Questioning the nurses on the primary causes for doctors' missed hours, 40 percent blamed "tolerance of these situations in the public health sector"; 39 percent identified "ineffective supervisory and control measures"; only 12 percent, though, suggested "low pay." This last result is important since pay is a principal argument for explaining why doctors hold several jobs with overlapping hours.

Asked what the consequences of these unjustified absences were, 27 percent of nurses listed "delaying or hindering activities at the times and in the form required," which obviously generates more inefficiency in the use of public resources. Another 26 percent thought that these absences were responsible for "generating a bad image for the institution," and 26 percent thought it "lower[ed] the quality of care." In the competitive market that has emerged from the recent reforms, the net effect of absenteeism is to undermine the competitiveness of public hospitals.

Institutional Characteristics of Bogota's Public Hospitals

The public hospitals in Bogota are not homogeneous in their institutional features, nor are their levels of reported irregular conduct, although they are all subject to the same rules. The unequal levels of development after the 1993 health reform appear to derive from different restrictions or at least different degrees of restriction, which could be overcome to some extent by adapting to the new institutional scheme. To better understand the factors that contribute to corruption, it is worth focusing on the variety of organizational schemes among these hospitals, particularly with regard to differing degrees of independence, transparency and management, and supervision and control.

All public hospitals in Bogota appear to have considerable independence under the new system. The district hospitals operate under the same regulatory framework, which according to Bossert (1997) would imply that they theoretically all have the same room for action or space for formal decision making. Moreover hospital directors perceive that they have considerable independence. In fact, under the new system most hospitals consider that the Health Ministry rarely or never intervenes in their principal operations (budget preparation, hiring, and purchase of inputs), in clear contrast to the situation before decentralization and the health reform, when the Ministry was the principal actor (see Table 6.5).

However this independence is less clear with regard to the SDS, the public entity responsible for management and leadership in the health sector at the district level. This is especially evident in the process of budget preparation and general management. Some 90 percent of the hospitals report that the District Secretariat is permanently involved in these functions.

SDS's involvement is not surprising in view of the continuing importance of government subsidies in financing public hospital budgets. The SDS must be concerned with the solvency of the district government, which can be strongly affected by hospital spending since such health expenditures represented fully 8 percent of the district's budget in 1998. In that same year, the SDS did generate revenues from sale of hospital services to private insurers, but this income represented only 10 percent of total hospital expenditures, on average. The remaining 90 percent of expenditures were still financed by the SDS as a direct subsidy for services provided.

The degree to which public hospitals differ in their independence from the SDS is tied to their relative ability to achieve financial independence through income generated from sales of services. In general, they have a small share of the subsidized insurance market that covers the poor population. For example, in 1998 the SDS allocated Col$ 90 billion to pay subsidized premiums for low-income households, yet public hospitals were able to capture only about Col$ 22 billion of this amount. Despite this relatively small market share, the public hospitals vary enormously in their respon-

Table 6.5 Hospital Autonomy: Perceived Rate of Supervisory Agency Intervention, 1999 (In percent)

	Always	Sometimes	Rarely	Never
How often does the agency intervene in annual budget preparation?				
SDS	91	0	0	9
Ministry of Health	3	6	22	69
How often does the agency intervene in procurement?				
SDS	9	16	9	66
Ministry of Health	3	3	3	91
How often does the agency intervene in hiring civil service staff?				
SDS	44	25	3	28
Ministry of Health	0	0	9	75
How often does the agency intervene in hiring nonpermanent staff?				
SDS	0	10	3	87
Ministry of Health	0	7	3	90
How often does the agency intervene in setting pay for civil service workers?				
SDS	39	7	0	55
Ministry of Health	13	7	3	77
How often does the agency intervene in setting pay for nonpermanent staff?				
SDS	0	3	3	94
Ministry of Health	0	3	0	97

Source: Survey of key informants.

Note: Figures represent the share of hospital directors' responses to survey questions.

siveness to the market. The share of hospital expenditures provided by sale of services under the new insurance scheme ranged from as low as 2 percent to almost 50 percent in 1998 (see Table 6.6). Thus the real maneuvering room of the district hospitals depends not so much on their status as State Social Enterprises, which gives them de jure freedom, but on the financial independence conferred by the payments each receives from nongovernmental insurers, above and beyond the funds directly or indirectly allocated by the District Health Secretariat.

With respect to the independent management of human resources, 44 percent of the hospital directors thought that the Secretariat "always" intervenes in the hiring of permanent staff, and nearly as many (39 percent) identified intervention in setting permanent staff wages. Pay levels are set by the district council — the highest regional authority, which has regulatory power and supervisory and control functions over other district bodies (see Table 6.5).

This reflects continuing limitations over management of human resources, although the hospitals have considerably more independence in managing contracted (nonpermanent) staff. If 77 percent of hospital directors said that the Health Ministry always intervenes in setting wages for permanent staff (nearly double the rate for SDS), *no* hospital director reported intervention in determining the pay of contracted staff (Table 6.5). Since about three-quarters of hospital expenditure goes to pay salaries (Giedion and Morales, 1999), the restrictions on managing personnel can severely constrain those hospitals with a high share of permanent staff. To circumvent this rigidity, many district hospitals have opted to use temporary contracted personnel who are not subject to civil service regulations.

Public hospitals use their margin of independence in the management of human resources differently, with large variations between hospitals. In 1998 the average share of contracted staff to total staff was 33 percent, but the range varied between lower and upper bounds of 12 percent and 91 percent. Although independent personnel management is limited in the aggregate, a few hospitals are making extensive use of contracted staff (see Figure 6.3).

In summary, public hospitals appear to have significant independence from the national Ministry of Health, which was omnipotent before the 1993 reforms. At the same time, some of this newfound independence is constrained by the local government (SDS), and maneuvering room remains extremely limited in managing permanent staff. The district hospitals vary in their financial independence from the SDS, with some institutions financing substantial portions of their expenditures from sales of services. In general, however, the public hospitals have not captured a substantial portion of the potential market. Hospital independence is also differentiated with regard to the proportion of staff members who are hired under more-flexible, nonpermanent contracts not bound by the civil service codes.

Figure 6.3 Distribution of Bogota District Hospitals by Share of Nonpermanent Contract Staff

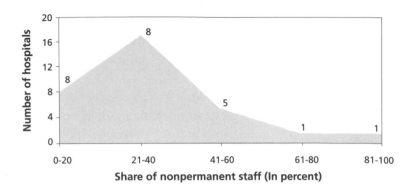

Share of nonpermanent staff (In percent)

Transparency, Accountability, and the Uses of Information

In 1998, on average, 63 percent of district hospital income was received from billing for services to patients — who were covered either by the District or nongovernmental insurers in the subsidized (ARS) and contributive (EPS) schemes. The other 37 percent came from the SDS through direct payment to the hospitals and without any specific mechanism for accountability.

Moreover, there are major differences between hospitals in the proportion of income received from provision of services. Between 1997 and 1999, some hospitals received about 87 percent of their total income from billings, while others were only able to bill 16 percent (see Table 6.6). This mixed scheme of incentives — income from services alongside a public subsidy to cover almost any deficit — means that hospitals are not accountable in any real sense for the use of their funds.

In addition to the allocation mechanism, effective accountability requires a set of basic management tools to provide reliable information. Such tools include development plans, annual budgets with regular budget review, and investment plans, along with targets for production, productivity, and quality. In 1998, 80 percent of the hospitals lacked these basic management tools.

Table 6.6 Share of Public Hospital Income from Nongovernmental Insurers (In percent)

	From ARS and EPS			From all sources (ARS, EPS, and SDS)		
	1997	1998	1999	1997	1998	1999
Average	5	10	9	47	63	71
Lowest	0	2	0	31	16	48
Highest	22	46	19	68	87	91
Median	3	8	8	—	—	—

Source: District Secretary of Health.

Note: Figures represent the share of income in the District of Bogota's 32 public hospitals that comes from reimbursement for services provided to policyholders with Empresas Promotoras de Salud (EPSs), Administradoras del Régimen Subsidiado (ARSs), and the Secretaría Distrital de Salud (SDS).

In the specific case of procurement, many hospitals lack instruments as essential as a purchase plan with minimum and maximum inventory quantities, data on average consumption and replacement times, and a kardex recording system. Only 4 of the 32 district hospitals had procurement plans, and only 17 percent had a kardex register — perhaps the most elementary tool for managing supplies.

Having information and management tools will not make a difference if they are not wielded by someone interested in controlling irregularities. Health reform addressed this problem by creating hospital boards comprised of representatives from the hospital, the district, and the local community. In 1998, all 32 hospitals had a board of directors, which met on average about twice a month with all members (in 6 hospitals) or nearly all members (in 19 hospitals) usually in attendance (see Table 6.7). In the surveys, 20 hospitals reported active participation by the boards, suggesting there is active community involvement in public hospital management.

Supervision and Control in District Hospitals

As mentioned earlier, Colombia is characterized by excessive regulation and a large number of control agencies that are supposed to provide the "stick"

Table 6.7 Role and Attendance Records of Hospital Boards, 1999

	Number of Hospitals
Attendance by Board of Directors	
All directors attend	6
Occasionally one member absent	19
Occasionally several members absent	4
Frequently one or more members absent	3
Role performed by Board of Directors	
Attend meetings to be briefed	5
Attend but participate in no major decisions	13
Attend, comment upon, and participate in some decisions	20
Attend, comment upon, and participate in all decisions	6
Total number of district hospitals	32

Source: Interviews with hospital directors and key informants.

Note: Figures may not add up due to multiple responses.

to control corruption. It is difficult to calculate the total cost of these control agencies, but Bogota notably earmarks about 8 percent of its overall budget for control agencies devoted to inspection and supervision, and for the pay of officials who work exclusively in control and supervision.

In the survey of 32 Bogota hospitals, over 50 percent of staff members acknowledged the existence of supervisory and control mechanisms for preventing irregular conduct in their institutions (see Table 6.8). However when staff members were asked why different types of irregular conduct occurred, the main answer was that those supervisory and control mechanisms are weak. Almost half of respondents blamed high absenteeism on poor supervision and control, and 60 percent blamed theft on the same inadequacy (see Table 6.9). Apparently supervisory and control mechanisms are largely formal and are ineffective in practice.

Supervision and control need not rely solely on formal mechanisms. In many contexts, people feel that social norms and concern for personal reputation not only lead one to conform to legal and acceptable behavior, but also to denounce an irregular activity when it is observed. No such environment appears to function in the surveyed public hospitals, since a large

Table 6.8 Staff Perceptions of Oversight Mechanisms for Preventing Irregularities (In percent)

Are there supervisory and control mechaninsms in your hospital to control . . .	Yes	No	Don't know
Unjustified absence by medical staff	62	31	7
Mismanagement of procurement	50	38	12
Theft of materials or equipment	58	32	10
Unauthorized use of equipment, facilities, and medical supplies	52	36	12
Unauthorized charges to patients	59	28	13

Source: Survey of doctors, nurses, and administrative personnel.

share of staff thought that reporting irregular conduct to authorities would lead to reprisals. Thus 65 percent of people who were aware of some irregular act "did nothing" about reporting it, and 85 percent said it was because of "fear of reprisals." On average, respondents reported that the ratio of detected offenses to total staff was approximately 7 percent, although this result varied widely across hospitals.

In summary, although public hospitals now have the minimum tools to implement supervision and control, survey results indicate that they are

Table 6.9 Reasons Given by Staff for Irregularities (In percent)

	Share of Staff	
Reasons given for . . .	Doctors' absenteeism	Theft
Low pay	15	8
Work shifts that are too long	6	—
Tolerance of such behavior by the public sector	33	20
Deficient supervisory and control mechanisms	46	60
Other reasons	—	11
Total	100	100

Source: Survey of doctors, nurses, and administrative personnel.

ineffectively applied and frequently inappropriate for the community and the institution, a situation that is aggravated by fear of reprisals.

Valuing Institutional Factors as Deterrents

In this section, a multivariate statistical analysis is used to see whether the variations in institutional design across hospitals are associated with different levels of corruption. In particular, the analysis focuses on whether or not the level of independence, generation and use of information, participation by interested parties, and supervision and control in hospitals are correlated with levels of corruption, after controlling for other factors.

Evaluating Price Differentials as Evidence of Corruption

As noted earlier, hospitals paid widely differing prices for supplies. These prices also differed significantly from the reference prices that were negotiated by Red Salud. These variances might be justifiable. For example there might be different transportation costs, discounts for volume, or extra charges for late payment or urgent delivery. However most such differences among these hospitals are fairly small. They are all in the same city, the same local market, and within close proximity. In order to see whether the price differences are important and whether they are systematically correlated with the institutional variables that we have identified, a number of control variables will be used in a multivariate regression.

The independent variable in the analysis is price variations. For simplicity and comparability, the prices were normalized around the reference prices negotiated by Red Salud. Hence the independent variable was actually the percentage difference between the price paid and the reference price. These price "gaps" were regressed on three types of variables: those associated with the purchase process itself, those related to the institutional characteristics of the hospitals, and lastly those associated with the individual characteristics of the purchase manager. The explanatory variables used are presented below with an indication of their expected relationship with the price gaps.

The explanatory variables associated with the procurement process included volume, forms of payment, type of supplier (wholesale or retail), credit terms, and type of bidding arrangement. Presumably hospitals that purchase in larger amounts should be able to negotiate volume discounts, and therefore would have relatively lower prices (*volume*). Suppliers are also likely to charge higher prices to buyers who do not regularly pay on time (*late payment*). Hospital transactions with retail establishments are likely to be higher than those with wholesalers who generally have lower average fixed costs and distribution costs (*retail*). Prices are also likely to be higher when the hospital has more time to pay the bill (*grace period*). Finally, direct procurement is likely to yield higher prices than open bidding since the latter, if done properly, disciplines suppliers through competition (*competitive bidding*).

The previous variables are introduced as controls. Our main interest is in the institutional variables that may or may not inhibit corruption. Based on the previous discussion, we hypothesize that a higher degree of implementation of the reform, measured as greater independence, would be associated with smaller divergence from the reference price. Moreover, better information and more participation by interested parties should tend to reduce prices by inhibiting irregular conduct. And the existence and effectiveness of supervisory and control mechanisms should also tend to inhibit irregular activity and be associated with smaller price gaps.

To measure hospital independence, the share of total staff members who are hired under nonpermanent contracts was used (*nonpermanent staff*). These contractual relationships varied significantly between hospitals and have a significant impact on the managerial discretion of the hospital director. Presumably hospitals with more of these nonpermanent employees can better control their staff if, in addition, there are effective accountability mechanisms.

To measure accountability, four indicators were used that are related to the possibility of generating information and to participation by the interested parties who will use that information. The first variable is the share of total hospital income that comes from billings to the District Health Secretariat and insurers (*billing share*). As the allocation of resources to public hospitals depends increasingly on their actual production of services, and not on historical spending levels, the space for concealing irregular conduct should diminish and, therefore, lower prices should be observed.

Accountability should also be higher in hospitals that derive a substantial share of their revenues from billings to insurers (*insurer share*) because the hospitals are more fully exposed to the market for services and are under greater pressure to control costs. These incentives encourage greater vigilance against irregular conduct. A larger share of billings to insurers should be associated with prices closer to the reference prices.

The tools available to management for controlling irregular conduct are another important institutional factor. A variable was created equal to the proportion of basic management tools (*management tools*), using a list of seven items prepared with the help of experts, that are operative in a hospital. These tools are (a) development plans, (b) annual income budgets, (c) investment plans, (d) production targets, (e) efficiency and productivity targets, (f) quality targets, and (g) institutional missions. Presumably using such tools introduces transparency into the management of the institution, which thereby can reduce irregular conduct.

Similarly a hospital's tools for managing medical and surgical supplies may affect its ability to control corruption (*supply management*). Based on a list of four items prepared with the help of experts, another variable was created equal to the proportion of these items that are available in the hospital. The tools are (a) purchase plans that establish minimum and maximum prices, (b) purchase plans related to average consumption, (c) information on replacement times, and (d) a kardex. As in the previous case, it is assumed that the availability of these tools reduces irregular conduct by introducing greater transparency into management.

A final institutional factor is related to the tools available for supervision and control of staff (*supervision*). A new variable was created equal to the proportion of six supervisory and control tools, identified with the help of experts, that the hospital had at its disposal. These tools are (a) internal disciplinary control offices, (b) complaints and claims offices, (c) complaint hotlines, (d) staff bonuses, (e) external audits, and (f) statutory audits. These control tools should improve the ability to monitor and discipline staff, thereby discouraging irregular activities and reducing the difference between the prices paid and the reference prices.

A third class of variables was introduced to consider the potential impact of differences among purchasing managers. First, the hospital purchase manager's income (*income*) was included under the presumption that better-paid managers are less likely to engage in corrupt activities and will therefore be associated with hospitals that pay less for supplies. Second, the purchase manager's sex was included to assess any systematic differences between men and women (*female*). Many studies argue that women

Table 6.10 Determinants of Variations in Supply Prices

Variables	Full sample		Procurement by bidding		Procurement by purchase order	
Constant	**3.334**	*2.622*	**3.626**	*2.904*	–3.044	*–1.201*
Characteristics of purchasing process						
Volume						
(coef. x 10⁻⁷)	4.47	*0.158*	–40.70	*0.677*	—	
Late payment	–0.106	*–1.010*	–0.058	*–0.469*	—	
Retail	0.098	*1.003*	0.061	*0.535*	—	
Competitive bidding	0.092	*1.494*	—		—	
Grace period						
(coef. x 10⁻²)	–0.050	*–1.203*	0.020	*0.255*	—	
Institutional factors						
Nonpermanent staff	**–0.722**	*2.755*	**–1.016**	*–3.152*	**–7.759**	*–4.633*
Billing share	**–0.559**	*–1.977*	**–0.832**	*–2.950*	**–5.271**	*–2.419*
Supply management	–0.088	*–0.692*	0.679	*0.500*	**2.471**	*4.171*
Management tools	**0.268**	*2.345*	**0.408**	*3.020*	**3.920**	*3.722*
Supervision	**0.295**	*4.439*	**0.365**	*5.423*	—	
Insurer share	–0.009	*–1.248*	–0.114	*–1.366*	—	
Characteristics of purchase managers						
Income						
(coef. x 10⁻⁷)	–4.040	*–2.028**	**–6.450**	*2.651*	**32.700**	*3.104*
Female	**0.191**	*2.389*	**0.293**	*2.420*	**2.685**	*2.655*
Married	**0.115**	*2.493*	**0.135**	*3.025*	**0.787**	*3.987*
Experience						
(coef. x 10⁻²)	0.003	*0.074*	0.010	*0.344*	**–1.930**	*–5.440*
Specialized education	**–0.147**	*2.352*	–0.075	*–1.184*	**–1.225**	*–4.582*
Observations	452		380		72	
R²	0.33		0.33		0.63	
F statistic	**43.71**		**21.51**		**39.26**	
F Probability	**0.0000**		**0.0000**		**0.0000**	
Joint F Prob. that all institutional coef. are zero	**0.0000**		**0.0000**		**0.0000**	

Notes: Boldface indicates statistically significant at the 5% level. An asterisk indicates statistically significant at the 10% level. T-statistics are indicated by italics.

are less likely to engage in irregular practices, so this coefficient would be expected to be negative. Third, experience in the public sector (measured by years of service) may be associated with higher levels of irregular conduct (*experience*). Officials with long service have more knowledge of opportunities for violating the law and may be better prepared to conceal misconduct. If purchase managers with more experience pay lower prices for supplies, this might indicate that experience leads to greater efficiency in purchasing. By contrast, if greater experience is associated with higher prices, after controlling for other factors, it may be an indication of corruption.

A fourth characteristic of purchase managers included in the analysis was marital status (*married*). This could discourage irregular conduct because family responsibility would increase risk aversion, or it could encourage irregular conduct because of the need to meet greater economic responsibilities.

The final personal characteristic is the manager's level of education, particularly whether or not specialized training was received that could affect the propensity to engage in corrupt activities (*specialized education*). For example, people with tertiary education, which is infrequent in Colombia, could be associated with greater academic ambition and stronger principles. On the other hand, completing higher education could be associated with greater personal ambition, desire for wealth, and cleverness in manipulating the system. Hence this factor could have a positive or negative impact.

Since information about the purchasing managers was not available for all of the hospitals, the analysis used data from only 22 of the 32 hospitals, creating a study sample of 452 transactions. Furthermore the standard errors must be corrected because the related series of data have different degrees of aggregation. Although the study had a series of 452 observations of price differences, the explanatory variables (institutional or individual) that relate to one hospital or one purchase manager are repeated for each transaction in a given hospital and are therefore not independent. In particular, the t-statistic can be biased upward by common errors of the group as shown by Moulton (1986). Blanchflower and Oswald (1990, 1994, and 1995) demonstrate how to estimate unbiased coefficients under such conditions through a correct specification of the effects of aggregate variables.

The analysis began with a set of OLS regressions with robust errors, grouped by hospital clusters and with control dummies for the purchase month and the particular item. In correcting for the aggregate effects, estimates were made for random effects, but they were not conclusive given the results of Breusch Pagan tests, which found that the variance of the errors is not different from 0 (see last row of Table 6.10).

The best results were obtained from OLS with robust errors and clustered by hospital. Three regressions were run. The first used data from the complete sample, while the second and third used data from transactions by bidding process and by purchase order, respectively. As will be seen later, the creation of the latter subsample substantially increased the explanatory power of the regression (see Giedion et al., 2001, Annex 5 for a complete summary of the explanatory variables used in the regressions).

The variables associated with the purchasing process (*volume, late payment, retail, competitive bidding, grace period*) were not significant in the first two regressions and were eliminated from the small sample of purchase orders.

In contrast, among the institutional variables the relationship with contracted staff was, as expected, highly significant. This confirms the hypothesis that a more independent management of human resources (*nonpermanent staff*) reduces overpayments for supplies. Moreover, all the regressions indicate that the price gap decreases as income from sale of services (*billing share*) increases. To some extent, this confirms the reliability of this indicator as a proxy for accountability since it is difficult to imagine that the billing share would have an impact for any other reason. Maintaining their significance and sign throughout the procedure, the two variables related to hiring and funding mechanisms appear to be the most solid of the institutional factors. This is interesting because it reflects a very real change in the working of the hospital, especially in relation to the incentives for the hospital in general (funding mechanisms) and the staff in particular (form of hiring).

Formal management instruments did not have the expected impact. In particular, having a development plan was statistically significant in all the regressions but associated with higher prices, not lower ones. Likewise, the existence of formal control mechanisms (*supervision*) was associated with higher price gaps. More surprisingly, the use of basic tools related to supply purchases, such as kardex or purchase plans, is not significant in the first two regressions. Only in the sample of direct purchase orders do these tools appear to have a significant effect, but again the effect is the reverse of what was expected.

With respect to the characteristics of the purchase manager, marital status and sex are significant and maintain their sign in all regressions. Prices are lower when the purchase manager is unmarried or a woman. Although the purchase manager's income is significant, the variable changes sign in the last regression and is highly significant. An inverse relationship is confirmed between income level and the price gap only in the first two regressions. Finally, the price gap appears to be lower as educational level rises. Overall the regression improves when the sample is restricted to transactions that were not subject to bidding. The explanatory power, as indicated by the R^2, almost doubles from 0.33 to 0.63 for the regression on this subsample (see Table 6.10); and the coefficients of our two principal explanatory variables of interest, the billing share and the proportion of nonpermanent staff, significantly increase.

The Impact of Institutional Variables on Absenteeism

To explore possible relationships between absenteeism and institutional factors, the information obtained from the survey of staff perceptions was used to construct a proxy for absenteeism. This variable (*Perceived absenteeism*) is the share of staff members in each hospital who stated they were aware of absenteeism among doctors in their facility. The absentee rate derived from

Table 6.11 Relationships between Perceived Absenteeism of Doctors and Institutional Variables

Variables	Correlation with perceived absenteeism of doctors
Billing share	−0.048
Management tools	−0.084
Nonpermanent staff	−0.446*
Number of board meetings per month	0.276
Staff perception of supervisory effectiveness	−0.061
Rate of disciplinary offenses	0.248

Note: Asterisk indicates statistically significant at the 10% level.

the census of nurses mentioned earlier was not used since the respondents were reluctant to answer questions about this issue. The resulting sample of hospitals for which there are responses is, therefore, unfortunately very small. Consequently the following analysis is limited to a simple exploration of pairwise correlations. There were too few degrees of freedom to conduct a multivariate analysis. Furthermore it should be emphasized that perceived absenteeism is only a very rough indicator, and all the qualifications made earlier apply.

The association between perceived absenteeism and several institutional variables was explored. In addition to the billing share, the existence of management tools, and the share of nonpermanent staff, we considered the number of board meetings per month as an indicator of how active a board might be in supervising and monitoring its hospital. We also looked at the staff perception of supervisory and control mechanism effectiveness, and the number of disciplinary actions that occurred, divided by the total number of staff. In the case of supervisory and control mechanisms, stronger mechanisms would be expected to be associated with less absenteeism. However the potential relationship with the rate of disciplinary actions is ambiguous since a high number of offenses could reflect a high incidence of irregular conduct or a more zealous and effective enforcement of rules.

An analysis of the correlation coefficients in Table 6.11 shows a significant inverse relationship between the perception of absenteeism and the percentage of contracted staff. The distinction between job status is important because it is almost impossible to "hire and fire" permanent staff, whereas less-rigid labor legislation makes it easier to manage nonpermanent staff. The inverse relationship suggests that absenteeism declines to the extent that it is within the directors' powers to dismiss employees whose performance is unsatisfactory.

None of the other correlations was statistically significant. However, three of the signs were in the expected directions. Thus the share of budget covered through selling services, the use of basic management tools, and the perception that these mechanisms are effective were all inversely related to the perception of absenteeism. The positive statistical association between the number of monthly board meetings and absenteeism among doctors is difficult to explain. It could, as in the case of the incidence of disciplinary actions, reflect more intense activity and supervision at hospitals that have more problems.

Conclusions

Contrary to the aims of Colombia's health-sector reform, Bogota's district hospitals are far from being independent in terms of human resource management and financial independence. Although some progress has been made in introducing modern management principles — independence, transparency and accountability, and supervision and control — the evidence obtained through interviews and surveys shows that in many instances the institutional advances are shallow and have not been implemented fully. Progress toward more independent management fundamentally depends on the incentives built into the reforms. Yet most hospitals have put off restructuring and moving toward reimbursements for services provided, which would generate the revenues and skills needed to be more independent. Instead they have continued to rely on government outlays to cover their deficits — irrespective of how much service is actually provided to the public — backed by political pressure and support from sectors opposed to reform. In 1998 the hospitals were still receiving 47 percent of their operating funds from direct subsidies; and, on average, 67 percent of hospital staff were working under the inflexible regulations of the administrative civil service and collective agreements that strongly limit independent management of personnel — a hospital's most important resource.

The implementation of the reform process was not without its faults. Perhaps the worst failure was the indefinite freezing of the transition period for hospitals required to calculate workers' pension liabilities, prepare formulas to integrate them into the new model, and recognize obligations up to 1994. In fact, none of this was done, and precious time was lost. A serious restructuring plan for Bogota's hospitals is only now being attempted, more than six years after the reform law and in the midst of a serious national economic crisis. This project aims to merge 15 of the 32 hospitals as a first step in adapting them to the new national health insurance system.

Despite the relatively timid steps toward implementing institutional changes within Bogota's hospitals, some hospitals progressed more than others. These variations made it possible to explore the relationship between institutional features and irregular conduct in the hospitals. Analysis confirmed that irregular conduct in procurement and in absenteeism among doctors, as reported by hospital staff in surveys, is related to institutional characteristics of the hospitals. The loss of public resources from paying supply prices in excess of reference prices may be as high as 10 percent of the budget allocation for purchasing medical-surgical supplies. This could have funded coverage for about 24,000 more poor people in the new public health insurance scheme. The resources lost through absenteeism among doctors were estimated to be about 5.7 percent of the budget, enough to insure an additional 12,000 people.

Hospital autonomy — in terms of greater discretion in personnel management and a greater share of income derived from reimbursement for services provided — is the one institutional factor that appears to have had a robust impact on reducing irregular conduct. In particular, there is a statistically robust and inverse relationship between the prices paid for supplies and the flexibility hospital directors get from employing larger shares of fixed-contract rather than permanent staff. While not ignoring some higher risks and the many disadvantages of hiring staff under such nonpermanent service contracts, the results of the correlations show that price gaps and levels of absenteeism decline as this form of employment increases. This relationship is confirmed by other studies that have documented how extremely rigid labor codes, which severely restrict personnel management capacity, exacerbate hospital inefficiency. Countries that have adopted employment contracts in which performance evaluation plays a role offer proof of the greater efficiency such systems have in providing access to public services.

The analysis also demonstrated the benefits for hospitals that took advantage of the ability to generate revenues through reimbursements for services provided to individuals who are insured with the District Health Secretariat or nongovernmental insurers. Hospitals that generated a larger share of their income from such reimbursements had more efficient procurement; they bought supplies at prices that were systematically closer to, or below, reference prices. Conversely, hospitals with lower billing shares paid higher supply prices. The billing share may generate stronger incentives to use resources more efficiently since the budget will depend on the services required by the population and not merely on historic levels of support to maintain hospital capacity independent of the population's needs. However, it appears that this relationship only holds when the billing share includes the District Health Secretariat, and not when restricted to billing of nongovernmental insurers.

Finally, it is important to recognize the practical value of research to measure and analyze irregular conduct. Corruption is generally invisible, but ways can be found to bring it to light. The estimated losses demonstrate the importance of controlling such irregular conduct, and better measurement of irregular conduct can help guide policy actions in that direction. For example, as a consequence of this study the District government implemented significant changes to reduce corruption in supply purchase agreements. During 2000, its first full year of implementation, information from the District Health Secretariat documented substantial cost savings from the revised procedures. In future studies, these new institutional designs should be evaluated so we can continue to learn about ways to combat corruption.

Surveys in Costa Rica and Nicaragua

A. Costa Rican Hospitals

The following tables are selected from a study that interviewed doctors, nurses, and patients in Costa Rican hospitals. Of the six hospitals surveyed, three participate in a system of annually negotiated management contracts with the Costa Rican Social Security Institute that owns and operates them. Over 1,400 people were surveyed during December 1998 and January 1999, including nurses (390), doctors (156), and patients (928). The major forms of illegal activity in these hospitals appear to involve absenteeism, and the use of public facilities/supplies to benefit private practices. The extent of absenteeism is most remarkable and is confirmed by over 90 percent of the nurses and doctors.

See Cercone et al. (2000) for full details regarding the survey, more tables, and an analysis of the impact of the management contracts on corruption.

— *Editors*

Table A.1 Surveyed Doctors, Nurses, and Patients, by Hospital

	Personnel			
Hospital	Doctors	Nurses	Patients	Total
With management contract	*90*	*272*	*486*	*848*
San Juan de Dios	40	213	188	441
San Vicente de Paul	20	26	149	195
Monseñor Sanabria	30	33	149	212
Without management contract	*66*	*118*	*442*	*626*
Guápiles	18	30	143	191
Max Peralta	16	33	164	213
San Rafael de Alajuela	32	55	135	222
Total	*156*	*390*	*928*	*1,474*

Source: Survey of personnel and patients.

Table A.2 Principal Characteristics of Surveyed Patients (In percent)

Sample characteristics	Share of patients
Women	74.5
Housewives	52.3
Employees (various income categories)	22.0
Between 14 and 34 years old	50.0
Over 60 years old	6.6
Completed primary schooling or less	56.5
Monthly household income below 30,000 colones per person	53.2
Used the inpatient facilities of this hospital	13.0
In the hospital for a consultation	48.3
In the hospital for inpatient services	26.1
Ever visited a private doctor	56.8
Came to hospital by bus or walking	56.5

Source: Survey of personnel and patients.

Note: At the time of the survey the foreign exchange rate was approximately 257 colones per U.S. dollar.

Table A.3 Average Respondents' Ratings of Corruption Levels in Costa Rican Institutions

Institution	Patients	Doctors	Nurses
Private schools	5.3	5.1	6.2
Ministry of Education	5.4	5.7	6.5
Ministry of Health	5.4	5.3	6.7
The media	5.6	6.1	5.8
Costa Rican Social Security Institute	6.1	6.8	7.6
Supreme Court of Justice	6.2	6.0	7.2
Government banks	6.3	6.8	7.6
Ministry of Public Works and Transportation	6.7	8.0	7.9
Tax Certification Authority	7.0	9.2	8.6
Presidency of the Republic	7.2	6.6	8.2
Traffic officers	7.6	8.5	8.4
Number of responses	482	125	348
No answer (%)	48.0	19.8	10.7

Source: Survey of personnel and patients.

Notes: Corruption levels were rated on a scale of 0 to 10, with 0 indicating no corruption and 10 indicating the highest degree of corruption. "Tax Certification Authority" is a rough translation for the *Certificado Abono Tributaria.*

Table A.4 Share of Respondents Giving Particular Reasons for Public Sector Corruption (In percent)

Reasons	Doctors	Nurses	Patients
Excessive and complex regulations	30.8	16.4	8.3
Weak laws	51.3	71.3	41.3
Lack of professionalism	36.5	52.3	38.6
Low salaries	57.1	40.3	35.7
Bad models from leadership	61.5	68.7	35.3
Poverty	16.7	26.4	35.3
Lack of education	19.9	23.6	23.3
Political interference	61.5	44.9	12.9
Insufficient economic reform	7.1	14.6	3.1
Excessive taxes	24.4	27.4	4.4
Lack of motivation at work	44.9	44.9	—
Number of responses	153	384	652
No answer (%)	1.9	1.5	29.7

Source: Survey of personnel and patients.

Table A.5 Share of Doctors and Nurses Who Perceive Corruption, by Type of Action (In percent)

Type of corruption	Doctors	Nurses
Evidence of physician absenteeism	79.5	97.8
Unauthorized charges to patients	85.4	90.1
Theft of equipment and supplies	71.2	82.9
Number of responses	113	328
No answer (%)	27.5	15.8

Source: Survey of personnel and patients.

Table A.6 Average Incidence of Corruption by Type

Type of corruption	Doctors	Nurses
Scheduling of operations	3.6	6.7
Use of operating rooms for private patients	3.9	7.1
Medical prescriptions	2.8	6.2
Laboratory exams	2.9	5.9
Waiting lists	4.2	7.5
Special exams	2.7	6.4
Unauthorized charges to patients	3.9	7.2
Hiring	3.1	5.6
Referring patients to private practice	3.5	7.1
Number of responses	107	282
No answer (%)	31.4	27.6

Source: Survey of personnel and patients.

Note: Incidence is rated on a scale of 0 to 10, with 0 indicating no corruption and 10 indicating the highest degree of corruption.

Table A.7 Shares of Patients Giving Particular Reasons for Delay in Care (In percent)

Reason	Share
The doctor arrived late	57.6
The doctor left early	3.2
The doctor was absent	2.8
The doctor did not arrive	3.0
The paperwork was lost	2.1
Other reason	31.4
Number of responses	907
No answer (%)	2.3

Source: Survey of personnel and patients.

Note: Shares do not add up to 100 due to rounding.

Table A.8 Views of Personnel on the Frequency of Doctor Absenteeism (In percent)

Frequency of absenteeism	Doctors	Nurses
Daily	64.0	63.9
One or two times per week	23.0	20.1
One or two times per month	6.0	5.3
Occasionally during the year	7.0	10.7
Number of responses	100	338
No answer (%)	35.8	13.3

Source: Survey of personnel and patients.

Table A.9 Share of Personnel Attributing Doctor Absenteeism to a Specific Cause (In percent)

Reasons	Doctors	Nurses
Low salaries	37.2	6.9
Lengthy shifts	11.5	16.4
Too much work	31.4	16.2
Lack of revenue from public sector	25.0	17.7
Lack of performance evaluations	26.9	49.2
Do not feel part of the organization	25.6	13.8
Directors tolerate permissive attitudes	34.0	65.6
By custom	20.5	32.3
Lack of motivation	30.8	11.5
Doctors work in different locations	25.6	68.7
Lack of control	17.4	66.1
Forms of contracting	16.7	11.0
Number of responses	153	385
No answer (%)	1.9	1.2

Source: Survey of personnel and patients.

Table A.10 View of Personnel on the Frequency of Using Public Facilities or Supplies to Treat Private Patients (In percent)

Frequency	Doctors	Nurses
Daily	20.6	47.6
At least once per week	35.1	37.5
At least once per month	16.5	10.7
Almost never	18.6	2.5
Never	9.3	1.6
Number of responses	97	317
No answer (%)	37.8	18.7

Source: Survey of personnel and patients.

Note: Shares do not add up to 100 due to rounding.

Table A.11 Distribution of Illegal Charges for Medical Consultations to Patients

Amount of charges	Number of responses	Cumulative share (%)
Less than 5,000 colones	7	24
5,000 to 10,000 colones	9	55
10,000 to 20,000 colones	3	66
20,000 to 40,000 colones	3	76
40,000 to 80,000 colones	4	90
80,000 colones or more	3	100

Source: Survey of personnel and patients.

Table A.12 View of Personnel on the Frequency of Theft (In percent)

Frequency	Doctors	Nurses
Much	14.7	22.3
Some	41.3	57.1
Little	44.0	20.6
Total	100.0	100.0
Number of responses	142	366
No answer (%)	8.9	6.1

Source: Survey of personnel and patients.

Table A.13 Share of Personnel Perceiving Corruption, by Type and Hospital (In percent)

	Doctors		Nurses	
Hospital management contract:	With	Without	With	Without
Type of corruption				
Absenteeism among doctors	78.8	80.3	97.6	98.4
Unauthorized charges to patients	84.2	87.5	89.5	92.2
Theft of supplies or equipment	**81.4**	**58.2**	84.4	81.3
Number of responses	113		328	
No answer (%)	27.5		15.8	

Source: Survey of personnel and patients.

Note: Boldface indicates a statistically significant difference at the 5% level.

Table A.14 Views of Personnel Regarding Corruption, by Occupation and Management Contract

Hospital management contract:	Doctors			Nurses		
	With	Without	Diff.	With	Without	Diff.
Type of corruption						
Scheduling of operations	3.8	3.4	0.4	6.8	6.5	0.3
Use of operating rooms for private patients	4.2	3.4	0.8	7.3	6.8	0.5
Medical prescriptions	2.6	3.0	−0.4	6.5	5.4	**1.1**
Laboratory exams	2.7	3.2	−0.5	6.2	5.0	**1.2**
Waiting lists	4.3	4.0	0.3	7.6	7.1	0.5
Special exams	3.0	2.3	0.7	6.6	5.7	**0.9**
Unauthorized charges to patients	4.1	3.5	0.6	7.1	7.3	−0.2
Hiring	3.4	2.6	0.8	5.8	5.0	**0.8**
Patient referral to private practice	3.3	3.7	−0.4	7.1	7.2	−0.1
Number of responses		107			282	
No answer (%)		31.4			27.6	

Source: Survey of personnel and patients.

Notes: Measures are on a scale of 0 to 10, with 0 indicating no corruption and 10 indicating the highest degree of corruption. Boldface indicates statistically significant at the 5% level.

B. Nicaraguan Hospitals

The following tables are selected from a study that interviewed doctors, nurses, and patients in three Nicaraguan hospitals. The survey included interviews with 377 members of public hospital staff and 369 patients. Although all three hospitals are owned and operated by the public sector, significant differences in management and perceptions of corruption existed among them. Overall a large share of medical personnel and patients believe that absenteeism, theft, and the use of public facilities/supplies to benefit private practices are common.

See Espinosa (2000) for full details regarding the survey, more tables, and a discussion of the context within which the survey took place.

— *Editors*

Table B.1 Sample Size: Survey of Personnel

Hospital	Doctors Sample	Doctors Share	Nurses Sample	Nurses Share	Other personnel Sample	Other personnel Share	All personnel Sample	All personnel Share
Alemán Nicaragüense	60	52.2	57	31.0	36	9.6	153	22.7
Antonio Lenín Fonseca	42	34.7	53	29.9	19	4.1	114	15.1
Roberto Calderón	42	41.2	49	23.8	19	5.1	110	16.1
All selected hospitals	144	42.6	159	28.0	74	6.1	377	17.8
All national hospitals	144	10.2	159	4.4	74	1.0	377	2.9

Source: Special survey of patients and personnel.

Table B.2 Sample Characteristics for Patients

	Hospitals			
	Roberto Calderón	Alemán Nicaragüense	Antonio Lenin Fonseca	Total
Total	101	169	99	369
Sex (%)				
Women	53	74	69	67
Men	47	26	31	33
Occupational status (%)				
Employee	18	15	15	16
Self-employed	26	19	18	21
Housewife	30	47	47	43
Retired	5	2	5	4
Unemployed	20	15	7	14
Dependent	2	2	7	3
Education (%)				
No schooling	25	18	37	25
Primary	33	40	32	36
Secondary	33	33	24	31
Technical	3	1	0	1
University	7	8	6	7
Income (córdobas)				
Avg. monthly household income	2,135	1,939	1,212	1,762

Source: Special survey of patients and personnel.

Notes: Only patients over 14 years of age were interviewed. The foreign exchange rate at the time of the survey (1998) was C$ 10.6 = US$1.

Table B.3 Share of Personnel Who Perceive Corruption in Hospital Management, by Hospital and Occupation (In percent)

Action	Hospitals			Personnel		
	Roberto Calderón	Alemán Nicarag.	A. Lenín Fonseca	Doctors	Nurses	Other personnel
Graft/overcharging	27	25	12	24	19	24
Purchase to benefit supplier	28	30	14	27	22	24
Personal use of public vehicle	41	46	32	45	45	20
Spending on activities unrelated to hospital services	45	40	26	41	40	24
Spending on improvements to benefit particular people	36	33	18	35	26	24
Differential treatment of patients via bill waivers	46	37	30	38	39	32
Theft of equipment	32	22	14	22	29	8
Theft of supplies	32	21	12	21	24	18
Diverting donations for personal use	46	29	32	34	41	23
Diverting funds	43	28	21	32	35	16
Apropriating revenues for personal benefit	38	20	18	26	28	15
Number of respondents	110	153	114	144	159	74

Source: Special survey of patients and personnel.

Note: Table reports share of respondents who classified the particular type of action as either very frequent or always.

Table B.4 Share of Personnel Who Perceive Corruption Among Doctors by Hospital and Occupation (In percent)

Action	Roberto Calderón	Alemán Nicarag.	A. Lenín Fonseca	Doctors	Other nurses	Personnel
Use of equipment for friends	36	32	32	24	41	32
Use of equipment for private patients	49	31	38	29	48	35
Arriving late	33	28	17	13	37	27
Leaving early	27	37	25	24	36	31
Being absent during work hours	25	30	18	15	30	31
Working fewer hours than required	13	16	11	10	14	18
Theft of public equipment	31	13	15	6	34	11
Theft of public supplies	17	8	10	6	16	11
Diverting donations to personal use	24	15	15	7	28	15
Number of respondents	110	153	114	144	159	74

Source: Special survey of patients and personnel.

Note: Table reports share of respondents who classified the particular type of action as either very frequent or always.

Table B.5 Average Patient Expenditures in Hospitals (In 1998 córdobas)

	Roberto Calderón	Alemán Nicaragüense	A. Lenín Fonseca	Average
Medical supplies	516.00	107.50	24.00	221.70
Emergency response	503.33	194.44	188.00	247.06
Exams	777.10	231.25	657.78	496.89
Medication	679.72	222.65	811.68	542.15
Average	619.04	188.96	420.37	376.95

Source: Survey of patients

Note: The average payment for similar hospitals was C$ 431 as reported in the 1996 demand survey conducted by the Ministerio de Salud Publica. Only one-third of patients in the survey reported any spending within the hospital.

Table B.6 Unit Costs for Hospital Services (In 1998 córdobas)

Services	R. Calderón	A. Nicaragüense	A. L. Fonseca
Inpatient	243.77	122.37	138.01
Outpatient	36.52	22.46	19.06
Emergency	121.88	61.18	69.00
Radiology	24.36	80.96	6.43
Laboratory	7.04	2.60	3.08

Source: Fiedler, John L. "Eficiencia, Financiamiento y Papel del Ministerio de Salud de Nicaragua: Un Análisis Retrospectivo y Prospectivo."

Table B.7 Resource and Productivity Indicators, by Hospital

	R. Calderón	A. Nicaragüense	A. L. Fonseca
Beds per doctor	2.28	1.78	2.42
Beds per nurse	1.13	1.11	1.66
Discharges per bed	27.90	99.46	36.25

Source: Table 1, in "Nicaragua: Sistema de hospitales públicos (Año 1998)."

Table B.8 Respondent Perceptions of Factors Affecting Probability of Detection (In percent)

	Roberto Calderón	Alemán Nicaragüense	Antonio Lenín Fonseca
Attitude of personnel who face illegal conduct			
Indifference	5	10	4
Denounce	8	23	11
Don't denounce	53	26	39
Reason for not denouncing			
Fear	41	46	27
Difficult procedures	5	4	3
Other	34	25	39
Don't know	13	18	19
Monitoring and sanctions for absenteeism			
Hospital directors tolerate absenteeism	19	26	22
Lack of monitoring	21	25	32
No sanctions for absenteeism	9	11	9
Poor quality of monitoring	21	14	18

Source: Special survey of hospital personnel.

Table B.9 Significance of Sanctions: Share Who Think a Particular Sanction is Likely (In percent)

	Roberto Calderón	Alemán Nicarag.	A. Lenín Fonseca	Doctors	Nurses	Other Personnel
Dismissal	44.6	69.9	43.4	62.5	46.0	66.1
Fines	3.6	2.2	4.8	3.8	2.9	3.4
Reprimand	22.9	5.1	8.4	5.8	14.4	11.9
Other	25.3	13.2	32.5	22.1	25.2	13.6
Don't know	3.6	9.6	10.8	5.8	11.5	5.1

Source: Special survey of hospital personnel.

REFERENCES

Ades, A., and R. Di Tella. 1995. "Competition and Corruption." Applied Economics Discussion Paper Series No. 169. Oxford University, Oxford, England.

———. 1997a. "National Champions and Corruption: Some Unpleasant Interventionist Arithmetic." *Economic Journal*. 107: 1023–42.

———. 1997b. "The New Economics of Corruption: A Survey and Some New Results." *Political Studies*. 45: 496–515.

———. 1999. "Rents Competition and Corruption." *American Economic Review*. 89 (4): 982–94.

Alcázar, L., and R. Andrade. 2000. "Transparencia y rendición de cuentas en los hospitales públicos: El caso Peruano." Latin American Research Network Working Paper R-383. Inter-American Development Bank, Washington, D.C.

Alesina, A., and B. Weder. 1999. "Do Corrupt Governments Receive Less Foreign Aid." NBER Working Paper No. 7108. National Bureau of Economic Research, Cambridge, Massachusetts.

Arrow, K. 1963. "Uncertainty and the Welfare Economics of Medical Care." *American Economic Review*. 53: 941–73.

———. 1985. "The Economics of Agency." In J. W. Pratt and R. J. Zeckhauser, editors. *Principals and Agents: The Structure of Business*. Boston: Harvard Business School Press.

Banerjee, A. 1997. "A Theory of Misgovernance." Mimeographed document. Department of Economics, Massachusetts Institute of Technology, Cambridge, Massachusetts.

Bardhan, P. 1997. "Corruption and Development: A Review of Issues." *Journal of Economic Literature*. 35 (September): 1320–46.

Barnum, H., and J. Kutzin. 1993. *Public Hospitals in Developing Countries: Resource Use, Cost, Financing*. Baltimore: Johns Hopkins University Press.

Becker, G. S. 1968. "Crime and Punishment: An Economic Approach." *Journal of Political Economy*. 76 (2): 169–217.

Becker, G., and G. Stigler. 1974. "Law Enforcement, Malfeasance, and Compensation for Employees." *Journal of Legal Studies*. 3 (1): 1–18.

Blanchflower, D., and A. Oswald. 1990. "The Wage Curve." *Scandinavian Journal of Economics*. 92 (2): 215–35.

___. 1994. "Estimating a Wage Curve for Britain 1973–90." *Economic Journal*. 104: 1025–43.

___. 1995. "An Introduction to the Wage Curve." *Journal of Economic Perspectives*. 9 (3): 153–67.

Blaug, M. 1980. *The Methodology of Economics*. Cambridge, England: Cambridge University Press.

Bliss, C., and R. Di Tella. 1997. "Does Competition Kill Corruption?" *Journal of Political Economy*. 105 (5): 1001–23.

Borenstein, S., and N. Rose. 1994. "Competition and Price Dispersion in the U.S. Airline Industry." *Journal of Political Economy*. 102: 653–83.

Bossert, T. 1997. "Decentralization of Health Systems: Decision Space, Innovation, and Performance." Data for Decision Making (DDM) Working Paper. Harvard University School of Public Health, Cambridge, Massachusetts.

Burki, S., and G. Perry. 1998. *Beyond the Washington Consensus: Institutions Matter*. The World Bank Latin American and Caribbean Studies Series: Viewpoints. Washington, D.C.: World Bank.

Burki, S., G. Perry, and W. Dillinger. 1998. *Beyond the Center: Decentralizing the State*. The World Bank Latin American and Caribbean Studies Series: Viewpoints. Washington, D.C: World Bank.

Caiden, G. E., and N.J. Caiden. 1998. "Enfoques y lineamientos para el seguimiento, la medición y la evaluación del desempeño en programas del sector público." *Revista Reforma y Democracia*. 12: Caracas: CLAD.

Cagan, P. 1958. "The Demand for Currency Relative to the Total Money Supply." *Journal of Political Economy*. (August): 303–28.

Campbell, T. 1997. "Innovations and Risk-Taking: The Engine of Reform in LAC." World Bank Discussion Paper No. 357. World Bank, Washington, D.C.

Cárdenas, M., and C. Darrás. 1997. "Documento preparatorio: Plan estratégico de salud." Mimeographed document. Ministerio de Salud, La Paz, Bolivia.

Cercone, J. A., F. Durán-Valverde, and E. Muñoz-Vargas. 2000. "Compromiso de gestión, rendición de cuentas y corrupción en los hospitales de la Caja Costarricense de Seguro Social." Latin American Research Network Working Paper R-418. Inter-American Development Bank, Washington, D.C.

CGBA (City Government of Buenos Aires Health Secretariat). 1997a. *Análisis comparativo de precios de compra y consumos para los insumos hospitalarios según modalidad del gasto existente*. Buenos Aires: CGBA.

___. 1997b. *Síntesis estadística*. Buenos Aires: CGBA.

Consorcio Hospitalario de Catalunya. Consultoría i Gestió, S.A. 1997. "Focalización de la inversión pública a nivel nacional e implementación del programa de atención integral a la salud: Primer informe." Mimeographed document. Report prepared for the Proyecto Salud – MSAS. Caracas, Venezuela: MSAS (August 22).

Di Tella, R. 1997. "Volver a sarmiento: Una propuesta para mejorar la eficiencia del gasto social basada en la competencia." Mimeographed document. Fundación Mediterránea, Buenos Aires.

Diéguez, H., J. Llach, and A. Petrecolla. 1990. "El gasto público y social." Report of Programa Nacional de Asistencia Técnica para la Administración de los Servicios Sociales en la República Argentina (PRONATASS), Buenos Aires.

Dmytraczenko, T., I. Aitken, S. Escalante Carrasco, K. Capra Seoane, K. J. Holley, W. Abramson, A. Saravia Valle, and M. Aparicio. 1998. "Evaluación del Seguro Materno Infantil en Bolivia." PHR Technical Paper No. 2347. Partnership for Health Reform, Bethesda, Maryland.

Espinosa Ferrando, J. 2000. "Rendición de cuentas y transparencia en los hospitales públicos de Nicaragua." Mimeographed document. Inter-American Development Bank, Washington, D.C.

Feldstein, P. 1993. *Health Care Economics*. 4th ed. Albany, New York: Delmar Publishers.

Fisman, R., and R. Gatti. 2000. "Decentralization and Corruption across Countries." Policy Research Working Paper 2290. World Bank, Washington, D.C.

Fundación Corona. 2000. "Resultados del estudio de probidad." *El Tiempo*. 6 April. (Bogotá, Colombia)

Gatti, R. 1999. "Explaining Corruption: Are Open Countries Less Corrupt?" Mimeographed document. World Bank, Washington, D.C.

Giedion, U., and C. Molina. 1994. "El sector de la salud: Desafíos futuros." *Revista Coyuntura Social.* 11: 71–87. (Bogotá, D.C., Colombia: Fedesarrollo)

Giedion, U., and L. Morales. 1997. "Aproximación a la medición de la eficiencia en los hospitales públicos del Distrito Capital." Mimeographed document. Fedesarrollo, Secretaría Distrital de Salud, Bogotá, D.C., Colombia.

___. 1999. *Medición de la eficiencia económica y de la gestión de los hospitales públicos del Distrito de Santafé de Bogotá.* Bogotá, Colombia: Secretaría Distrital de la Salud.

Giedion, U., L. Gonzalo Morales, and O. L. Acosta. 2000. "Efectos de la reforma en salud sobre las conductas irregulares en los hospitales públicos: El caso de Bogotá, Distrito Capital – Colombia." Latin American Research Network Working Paper R-426. Inter-American Development Bank, Washington, D.C.

Giussani, B., and F. Ruiz. 1997. "El proceso de descentralización y financiamiento de los servicios de educación y salud en Bolivia." Serie Reformas de Política Pública 48. CEPAL, Santiago, Chile.

Goel, R., and D. Rich. 1989. "On the Economic Incentives for Taking Bribes." *Public Choice.* 61 (3): 269–75.

González, M. 1997a. "Evaluation of Intergovermental Health Systems in Latin American and Caribbean Countries: Foundations of a Research Program." Mimeographed document. University of Pittsburgh, Pittsburgh, Pennsylvania.

___. 1997b. "Evaluación del sistema intergubernamental de salud de Venezuela (1990–1996): Una aproximación inicial." Mimeographed document. MSAS/BID/Banco Mundial, Caracas, Venezuela.

González García, G., and F. Tobar. 1997. *Más salud por el mismo dinero: La reforma del sistema de salud en Argentina.* Buenos Aires: Grupo Editor Latinoamericano-ISALUD.

Graham, C., and M. Naim. 1998. "The Political Economy of Institutional Reform." In N. Birdsall, C. Graham, and R. Sabot, editors. *Beyond Trade Offs: Market Reforms and Equitable Growth in Latin America.* Washington, D.C.: Brookings Institution Press/Inter-American Development Bank.

Gray, C. 1979. "Civil Service Compensation in Indonesia." *Bulletin of Indonesian Economic Studies.* 15 (March): 85–113.

Gray, C. W., and D. Kaufmann. 1998. "Corrupción y desarrollo." *Finanzas y desarrollo.* (March): 7–10.

Gray-Molina, G., editor. 1997. *Construyendo politicas publicas locales en Bolivia.* La Paz: Plural.

Gray-Molina, G., and C. H. Molina. 1997. "Popular Participation in Bolivia: Building Public Accountability from the Grassroots." Paper presented at the seminar "State Reform in Bolivia, 1993–1997" on April 30 at Harvard University, Cambridge, Massachusetts.

Gray-Molina, G., and K. O'Neill. Forthcoming. "Popular Participation: An Experiment in Grassroots Decentralization." In Jorge Munoz, editor. *Bolivia: The Art of Reform 1982–1997.* Cambridge, Massachusetts: Harvard Institute for International Development (forthcoming).

Gray-Molina, G., E. Pérez de Rada, and E. Yañes. 1999. "Transparency and Accountability in Bolivia: Does Voice Matter?" Latin American Research Network Working Paper R-381. Inter-American Development Bank, Washington, D.C.

Harvard School of Public Health. 1995. "La Reforma de salud y el plan maestro de implementación: Informe final." Mimeographed document. Cambridge, Massachusetts: Harvard School of Public Health.

Hines, J. 1995. "Forbidden Payments: Foreign Bribery and American Business after 1977." NBER Working Paper No. 5266. National Bureau of Economic Research, Cambridge, Massachusetts.

Hirschman, A. O. 1970. *Exit, Voice, and Loyalty: Responses to Declines in Firms, Organizations, and States.* Cambridge, Massachusetts: Harvard University Press.

Instituto APOYO. 1999. *La agenda de la primera década.* Lima, Peru: Instituto Apoyo.

Instituto Nacional de Estadística (INE). 1992. *Censo nacional de población y vivienda.* La Paz, Bolivia: INE.

_____. 1994. *Encuesta nacional de demografía y salud.* La Paz, Boliva: INE.

Instituto Venezolano de los Seguros Sociales (IVSS). 1998. *Avance del récord de estadísticas médico asistenciales año 1997: Versión preliminar.* Ministerio del Trabajo/Instituto Venezolano de los Seguros Sociales/Dirección General de Planificación, Programación y Presupuesto. Caracas, Venezuela: Instituto Venezolano de Seguros Sociales (May).

Inter-American Development Bank (IDB). 1996. *Making Social Services Work, Economic and Social Progress in Latin America, 1996 Report.* Washington, D.C.: Johns Hopkins University Press.

Jaén, M. H., and D. Paravisini. 1999. "Diseño institucional, estructura de incentivos y corrupción en hospitales públicos en Venezuela." Latin American Research Network Working Paper R-380. Inter-American Development ment Bank, Washington, D.C.

Jaén, M. H., S. Salvato, A. Briceño, J. Díaz Polanco, G. Padrón, D. Gómez Cova, C. Venot, B. Guzmán, J. Aparicio, L. Castillo, V. Aguirre, and L. Fuenmayor. 1997. "La reforma de salud en Venezuela." *Cuadernos para la reforma del sector salud,* 1:1. Caracas, Venezuela: Ministerio de Sanidad y Asistencia Social/Proyecto Salud.

Johnston, M. 1997. "The Search for Definitions: The Vitality of Politics and the Issue of Corruption." *International Social Sciences Journal.* 149: 321–35.

Kaufmann, D., and S. J. Wei. 1999. "Does Speed Money Grease the Wheels of Commerce?" Working Paper 2254. World Bank: Washington, D.C.

Kaufmann, D., A. Kraay, and P. Zoido. 1999. "Aggregating Governance Indicators." Policy Research Working Paper 2195. World Bank: Washington, D.C.

Keppel K., S. Taffel, and P. Placek. 1982. "Source of Hospital Payment for Deliveries in the United States, 1980." Paper presented at the Annual Meeting of the American Public Health Association, in Montreal, Canada.

Klitgaard, R. 1988. *Controlling Corruption.* Berkeley: University of California Press.

———. 1990. "Combatiendo la corrupción: Información e incentivos." *Nueva Sociedad.* 145.

———. 1991 *Adjusting to Reality: Beyond 'State Versus Market' in Economic Development.* San Francisco: International Center for Economic Growth/ICS Press.

___. 1992. *Controlando la corrupción*. La Paz, Bolivia: Quipus.

La Forgia, G. M. 1990. "Challenging Health Service Stratification: Social Security – Health Ministry Integration in Panama, 1973–1986." Doctoral thesis, University of Pittsburgh.

La Porta, R., F. Lopez-de Silanes, A. Shleifer, and R. Vishny. 1999. "JLEO Bureaucracy Conference: The Quality of Government." *Journal of Law, Economics, and Organization*. 15 (1): 222.

Lewis, M., G. M. La Forgia, and M. B. Sulvetta. 1996. "Measuring Public Hospital Costs: Empirical Evidence from the Dominican Republic." *Social Science Medicine*. 43 (2): 221–35.

Macho Stadler, I., and D. Pérez Castrillo. 1994. *Introducción a la economía de la información*. Barcelona, Spain: Ariel Economía.

Marjit, S., and H. Shi. 1998. "On Controlling Crime with Corrupt Officials." *Journal of Economic Behavior and Organization*. 34 (1): 163–72.

Mauro, P. 1995. "Corruption and Growth." *Quarterly Journal of Economics*. 110 (3): 681–712.

___. 1997. *Why Worry about Corruption*. Economic Issues No. 6. Washington, D.C.: International Monetary Fund.

___. 1998. "Corruption and the Composition of Government Expenditure." *Journal of Public Economics*. 69 (2): 263–79.

Mera J., E. Schargrodsky, D. Staffa, and F. Weinschelbaum. 1999. "Transparencia y rendición de cuentas en los hospitales públicos de América Latina." Advance report. Latin American Research Network, Inter-American Development Bank, Washington, D.C.

Ministerio de Salud. 1994. "La reforma de la seguridad social en salud." Ministerio de Salud, Bogotá, D.C., Colombia.

___. 1998. "Censo del recurso humano y dinámica salarial del sector salud oficial, 1994–1998." Ministerio de Salud, Bogotá, D.C., Colombia.

Ministerio de Salud y Desarrollo Social (MSDS). 1997. "Estadísticas hospitalarias año 1996." Dirección General Sectorial de Salud, Dirección Técnica de Servicios, Caracas, Venezuela.

___. 1998. "Estadísticas hospitalarias año 1997." Dirección General Sectorial de Salud, Dirección Técnica de Servicios, Caracas, Venezuela.

Ministerio de Salud Perú. 1996. "2do. Censo de infraestructura sanitaria y recursos del sector salud." Ministerio de Salud, Lima, Peru.

Molina, L., and U. Giedion. 1993. "Distribución de subsidios públicos en salud en Colombia." Mimeographed document. World Bank, Washington, D.C.

Mosqueira Medina, E. 1995. "El rol de las instituciones in la lucha contra la corrupción." *Contribuciones*. 12 (4): 105–26.

Moulton, B. 1986. "Random Group Effects and Precision of Regression Estimates." *Journal of Econometrics*. 32 (3): 385–97.

Myrdal, G. 1968. *Asian Drama: An Inquiry in the Poverty of Nations*. New York: Pantheon Press.

Nieves, I., G. La Forgia, and J. Ribera. 2000. "Large-Scale Government Contracting of NGOs to Extend Basic Health Services to Poor Populations in Guatemala." Case study presented at the IESE/World Bank/IDB conference The Challenge of Health Reform: Reaching the Poor, on May 24–26 in San José, Costa Rica.

North, D. 1990. *Instituciones, cambio institucional y desempeño económico*. México, D.F.: Fondo de Cultura Económica.

Ocampo Moreno, L. 1993. *In defensa propia: Cómo salid de la corrupción*. Buenos Aires: Editorial Sudamericana.

Organization of American States (OAS). 1996. Convención Interamericana contra la corrupción. Caracas, Venezuela, 29 March.

Palmier, L. 1983. "Bureaucratic Corruption and its Remedies." In M. Clarke, editor. *Corruption, Causes, Consequences and Control*. London: Frances Pinter.

Pan American Health Organization (PAHO). 1994. *Health in the Americas*. Washington, D.C.: PAHO.

____. 1998. *Health in the Americas*. Washington, D.C.: PAHO.

Paul, S. 1992. "Accountability in Public Services: Exit, Voice and Control." *World Development*. 20 (7): 1047–60.

____. 1994. "Does Voice Matter? For Public Accountability, Yes." Policy Research Working Paper 1388. World Bank, Washington, D.C.

Peterson, G. 1997. *Decentralization in Latin America: Learning through Experience.* The World Bank Latin American and Caribbean Studies Series: Viewpoints. Washington, D.C.: The World Bank.

Picciotto, R. 1997. "Putting Institutional Economics to Work: From Participation to Governance." In C. Clague, editor. *Institutions and Economic Development: Growth and Governance in Less-Developed and Post-Socialist Countries.* Baltimore and London: Johns Hopkins University Press.

Picciotto, R., and E. Wiesner. 1998. *Evaluation and Development: The Institutional Dimension.* London: Transaction Books.

Prats, J., and J. Company. 1996. "Barcelona Governance Project." Mimeographed document. Instituto Internacional de Gobernabilidad, Barcelona, Spain (July).

Pratt, J. W., and R. J. Zeckhauser, editors. 1985. *Principals and Agents: The Structure of Business.* Cambridge: Harvard Business School Press.

Prud'homme, R. 1995. "The Dangers of Decentralization." *World Bank Research Observer.* 10 (2): 201–21.

Rasmusen, E. 1996. *Juegos e información.* México, D.F.: Fondo de Cultura Económica.

Reinganum, J. 1979. "A Simple Model of Equilibrium Price Dispersion." *Journal of Political Economy.* 87 (4): 851–8.

Republic of Venezuela. 1983. Gaceta Oficial No. 32650, Decreto No. 1.798 del 21 de enero de 1983.

Rose-Ackerman, S. 1975. "The Economics of Corruption." *Journal of Public Economics.* 4 (2): 187–203.

____. 1978. *Corruption: A Study of Political Economy.* New York: Academic Press.

____. 1986. "Reforming Public Bureaucracy through Economic Incentives." *Journal of Law, Economics, and Organization.* 2 (1): 131–61.

____. 1998. "Corruption and Development." In B. Pleskovic and J. E. Stiglitz, editors. *Annual World Bank Conference on Development Economics 1997.* Washington, D.C.: World Bank.

Salop, S., and J. Stiglitz. 1977. "Bargains and Rip-offs: A Model of Monopolistically Competitive Price Dispersion." *Review of Economic Studies.* 44 (3): 493–510.

Salvato de Figueroa, S. 1998. "Financiamiento del gasto en salud en Venezuela." Mimeographed document. Universidad Católica Andrés Bello, Caracas, Venezuela.

Schargrodsky, E., J. Mera, and F. Weinschelbaum. 2000. "Transparencia y rendición de cuentas en los hospitales de América Latina: El caso de Argentina." Serie de documentos de trabajo R-382. Inter-American Development Bank: Washington, D.C. (February).

Shapiro, C., and J. Stiglitz. 1984. "Equilibrium Unemployment as a Worker-Discipline Device." *American Economic Review*. 74: 433–44.

Shleifer, A., and R. W. Vishny. 1993. "Corruption." *Quarterly Journal of Economics*. 108 (3): 599–617.

Svensson, J. 1999. "Who Must Pay Bribes and How Much." Mimeographed document. World Bank, Washington, D.C.

Tanzi, V. 1998. "Corruption around the World: Causes, Consequences, Scope, and Cures." IMF Working Paper WP/98/63. International Monetary Fund, Washington, D.C.

Tanzi, V., and H. Davoodi. 1997. "Corruption, Public Investment and Growth." IMF Working Paper WP/97/139. International Monetary Fund, Washington, D.C.

Thoene, B. 1999. "Posición de la Asociación Colombiana frente a la reforma de la ley 100 y la corrupción dentro del sistema de seguridad social en salud." *Revista Hospitalaria*. 1 (1): 6–8.

Transparency International Bangladesh. 1996. *Survey on Corruption in Bangladesh*. Dhaka, Bangladesh.

Treisman, D. 1998. "The Causes of Corruption: A Cross-National Study." Mimeographed document. UCLA, Los Angeles, California.

Tussing, D., and M. Wojtowycz. 1992. "The Cesarean Decision in New York State: Economic and Noneconomic Aspects." *Medical Care*. 30 (6).

____. 1993. "The Effect of Physicians' Characteristics on Clinical Behavior: Cesarean Sections in New York State." *Social Science Medical*. 37 (10): 1251–60.

Van Rijckeghem, C., and B. Weder. 1997. "Corruption and the Rate of Temptation: Do Low Wages in the Civil Service Cause Corruption?." IMF Working Paper WP/97/73. International Monetary Fund, Washington, D.C.

Vesga, R., et al. 1992. *La corrupción administrativa en Colombia.* Bogotá, D.C., Colombia: Fedesarrollo.

Walford, V., and K. Grant. 1998. *Health Sector Reform: Improving Hospital Efficiency.* London: Health System Resource Centre.

Walsh, J. 1998. "A World War on Bribery." *Time.* 22 June.

Wei, S. 1997. "How Taxing Is Corruption to International Investors?" NBER Working Paper No. 6030. National Bureau of Economic Research, Cambridge, Massachusetts.

World Bank. 1992. "Venezuela Health Sector Review." Vols. 1–2. Washington, D.C.: World Bank.

___. 1993. *World Development Report 1993: Investing in Health.* New York: Oxford University Press/World Bank.

Wouters, A. 1998. "Incentivos para mejorar la prestación de los servicios de salud: Métodos alternativos de pago a los proveedores." Mimeographed document. Partnerships for Health Reform (PHR), Abt Associates, Bethesda, Maryland.

Yellen, J. 1984. "Efficiency-Wage Models of Unemployment." *American Economic Review.* 74: 200–5.

CONTRIBUTORS

Olga Lucia Acosta is a Researcher at FEDESARROLLO, the Foundation for Higher Education and Development, in Colombia. She has an MsD. in Economics and Regulation from Paris University and has published articles in applied research in social and fiscal issues. She has been editor of *Revista Coyuntura Social* since 1997.

Lorena Alcázar is Chief Economist at Instituto APOYO. She is an active participant in national task forces aimed at improving health conditions and reducing poverty in Peru.

Raúl Andrade is Project Coordinator at Instituto APOYO in Lima, Peru.

Rafael Di Tella is Assistant Professor of Economics at the Harvard Business School in Cambridge, Massachusetts. He has published a wide range of articles on corruption in leading journals, including the *American Economic Review* and the *Journal of Political Economy*. He first addressed issues of corruption in the health sector while working for the Economics Ministry in Buenos Aires in 1996.

George Gray-Molina is a Research Associate at Fundación Dialogo of La Paz, Bolivia. He is additionaly affiliated with the Unidad de Análisis de Políticas Sociales, also in La Paz.

Ursula Giedion is currently a consultant at Bitran & Associates in Chile, and, at the time of the study, was working as a researcher with FEDESARROLLO in Colombia. She has an MA in Economics, has published articles on the reform of the health sector in Colombia, and was a senior advisor to the Ministry of Health.

María Helena Jaén is a Professor of Public Policy at the Center for Public Policy of the Instituto de Estudios Superiores de Administración (IESA) in Caracas, Venezuela. She has a Master's in Public Health from the University of Texas and a Ph.D. in Development Studies from the Centro de Estudios del Desarrollo (CENDES), Universidad Central de Venezuela. She has published articles and books on Venezuela's health system, health reform, and decentralization, and on nutrition and poverty.

Jorge Mera is a Senior Researcher at the Instituto Torcuato Di Tella, Buenos Aires, Argentina. He is an M.D., has an M.P.H. (Universidad de Buenos Aires), and has been a Post-Doctoral Scholar (University of California-Los Angeles). He has published several books and articles on health services delivery and reform of health services.

Daniel Paravisini is a Researcher at the Center for Public Policy of the Instituto de Estudios Superiores de Administración (IESA) in Caracas, Venezuela and is currently a Ph.D. candidate in Economics at the Massachusetts Institute of Technology (MIT) in Cambridge, Massachusetts. He has written on topics related to institutional development and reform in Latin America.

Luis Gonzalo Morales was a Researcher with FEDESARROLLO at the time of this study. He later served as Secretary of Health for the Department of Bogotá, and is currently providing support to health sector reforms in the Dominican Republic.

Ernesto Pérez de Rada is a Research Associate at Fundación Dialogo.

William D. Savedoff is a Senior Economist with the Social Programs and Sustainable Development Department of the Inter-American Development Bank. He has a Ph.D. in Economics from Boston University and has published articles and books of applied research on labor markets, urban development, education, and health in Latin America.

Ernesto Schargrodsky is a Professor at Universidad Torcuato Di Tella, Buenos Aires, Argentina, and a Visiting Professor at Stanford University, Palo Alto, California. He has a Ph.D. in Economics from Harvard University. His research concentrates on Industrial Organization and the Economics of Corruption and Crime.

Federico Weinschelbaum is Assistant Professor at the Universidad de San Andrés, Buenos Aires, Argentina. He has a Ph.D. in Economics from the University of California, Los Angeles (UCLA). His research focuses on game theory and information, and he is currently working on topics involving agency theory and the economics of corruption.

Ernesto Yañez is a Research Associate at Fundación Dialogo and is affiliated with the Unidad de Análisis de Políticas Sociales, both in La Paz.